C000157011

THE THOUGHTS OF

BETTY SPITAL

Christopher Meade

DERBYSHIRE
COUNTY LIBRARY
Matlock 7/92
3 0 MAR 1990
Bakewell
827 . 91 . MEA

PENGUIN BOOKS

Dedicated to Betty's lifelong companion
JANE JARMAN
with love, admiration and deepest sympathy

and also to Peter Meade

PENGUIN BOOKS

Published by the Penguin Group
27 Wrights Lane, London W8 5TZ, England
Viking Penguin Inc., 40 West 23rd Street, New York, New York 10010, USA
Penguin Books Australia Ltd, Ringwood, Victoria, Australia
Penguin Books Canada Ltd, 2801 John Street, Markham, Ontario, Canada L3R 1B4
Penguin Books (NZ) Ltd, 182–190 Wairau Road, Auckland 10, New Zealand

Penguin Books Ltd, Registered Offices: Harmondsworth, Middlesex, England

First published 1989

Copyright © Christopher Meade, 1989
All rights reserved

Photographs on p. 27 by Gina Glover, p. 41 by Cath Tate and p. 96 by Richard
Open/Camera Press.
All others by Caroline Laidler/IRIS.

Typeset, printed and bound in Great Britain by
BPCC Hazell Books Ltd
Member of BPCC Ltd
Aylesbury, Bucks, England
Typeset in 11/13pt Linotron 202 Sabon

Except in the United States of America,
this book is sold subject to the condition
that it shall not, by way of trade or otherwise,
be lent, re-sold, hired out, or otherwise circulated
without the publisher's prior consent in any form of
binding or cover other than that in which it is
published and without a similar condition
including this condition being imposed
on the subsequent purchaser

Editor's Preface

In a very real way the editing of this book has been something of a personal odyssey for me.[1]

Little did I realize on that cold winter morning, when I stood at the bus stop at the end of my road and happened to ask the little old lady who muttered beside me whether she knew the time of the next bus into town, that my life was about to be suddenly and irrevocably transformed.

By the time the double-decker arrived, I had already been subjected to a detailed political critique of Conservative public transport policy, the defects of government attitudes *vis-à-vis* the elderly, and the shortcomings of Sheffield Council's Refuse Collection Service.

By the time the bus turned into the High Street, the main points of the manifesto of the radical pensioners group of which Betty Spital is zealous supremo had been most forcefully outlined several times and she was berating the elderly gentleman beside me for his 'reactionary quietism in the face of the onslaught against his basic human rights'. (He had happened to yawn.)

By the time she had finished consuming the large cooked breakfast I was inveigled into buying her, I knew that this was no mere old lady but a unique piece of world history which sat before me in Mister B's Sandwich Bar, tucking into its second bacon butty.

It was then that it dawned on me, because Betty told me, that it was my duty to do everything in my power to help publish the Spital message to the world.[2] Thus began the mammoth task, the result of which is the book you hold.

1. Though in another way it hasn't.
2. A few brief words on the mode of recording employed may be pertinent here. Taped interviews were conducted with Ms Spital and transcribed in full with 'ums', 'ahs', contradictions, discontinuities and flatulence included, in keeping with our wish for absolute veracity to the as-it-is-lived experience of elderly persons and to ensure a textual discourse of complete accessibility to the broadest target community.

I cannot claim – Spital would not allow it – to have adequately conveyed the full richness of her personality in the editing of this humble work, and responsibility for all its flaws rests with me alone. But if this book in any way helps to rectify the atrocious distortions of the history books and reinstates the Spital name in its rightful place at the very centre of the political and cultural strands which make up the rich tapestry of our contemporary world view, then my life may once again become worth living.

Thanks are due to Jane Baker, Rachel Van Riel and Yorkshire Art Circus for their unstinting work on Betty's behalf, but it is of course to Ms Spital and her many comrades in SPLAF that I owe the most immense – and far from interest-free – debt.

CHRISTOPHER MEADE

However, the need to condense her original utterances soon became apparent. For instance, a section of tape transcribed thus: 'CM: And the war . . .?/ BS: Pardon?/ CM: The war./ (Sound of coughing) BS: Oh . . . aye?/ CM: Do you remember it at all?/ BS: Oh . . . aye./ (Pause)/ CM: Do any particular recollections spring to mind?/ (Pause. Coughing. Microphone rattle)/ BS: Ooh . . . aye./ CM: Do you think you might tell us something about them?/ (Pause)/ BS: Who did you say you were again?' These instances are signified here by a single space left between paragraphs.

Other sections have been edited for the sake of clarity. For instance, a somewhat lengthy section in which Ms Spital talks not entirely intelligibly about her theory of a conspiracy to defraud pensioners involving the CIA, the Royal Family, and the woman behind the cold meat counter in the Spitalcliffe Tesco's was eventually summarized as 'I can't say I hold with the Monarchy'.

After this initial transcription, Ms Spital and I worked on the text at regular evening meetings during which alterations, edits and light household chores were undertaken by myself in keeping with the Twerly dictum 'to each according to their seniority, from each according to their gullibility'.

At this point the text was discussed by the entire SPLAF oral history collective over a period of some days in the communal living-room of my own home – the site of which, interestingly enough, Ms Spital remembers from her early days as a Tiller Girl when a music hall existed on that very spot. In Ms Spital's own words: 'Local lads used to sneak in round the back way to spy on us changing, so it were full of little wankers even then.'

THE THOUGHTS OF

BETTY SPITAL

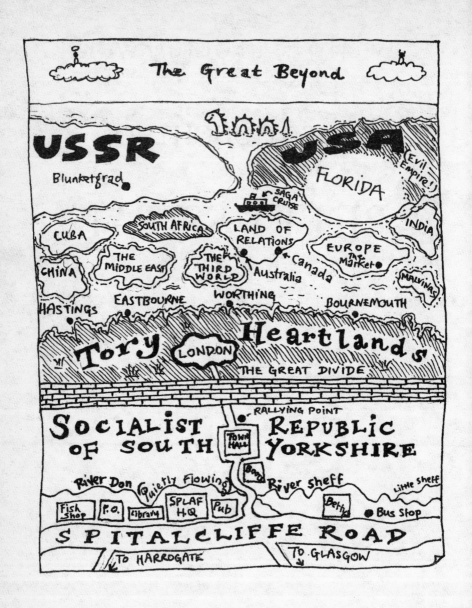

Twerly Map of the World

This map of the world is based upon the Spital Projection rather than the more familiar Mercator Projection.

The Spital Projection introduces several innovative characteristics: a subjectively accurate rendition of the relative importance of parts of the land surface area from a northern radical perspective; graphical representation of the centres of elderly population restored to the physical proportions their immense significance deserves; colour coding to denote states engaged in potentially pre-revolutionary struggle; symbols pinpointing the whereabouts of distant relations and decent fresh fish shops; and the entire world surface redesigned to make it look a bit neater.

This Projection represents an important step away from the prevailing Juvocentric geographical and cultural concept of the world.

CM: Your pensioners group must be a marvellous source of comfort and support to you in your autumn years, Betty.

Betty: *Oh, aye. I think it's very important for we old folk to have summat to occupy us.*

CM: Perhaps you could give us an idea of the activities you run?

Betty: *Just the usual, really: coffee mornings, old-tyme dancing, self-defence and sexuality workshops . . . that sort of thing.*

CM: How very enterprising!

Betty: *Keeps us out of mischief, I suppose.*

CM: And what are you busy with at present?

Betty: *Just a spot of shopping. Catering arrangements for next Monday's picket of the running dogs of Age Concern. I've to fetch ingredients for the Molotov Cocktails.*

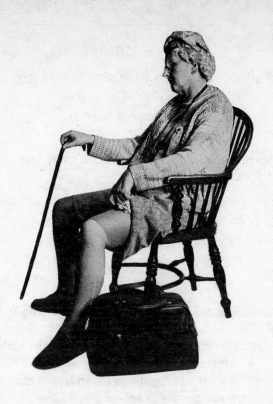

CM: But surely you wouldn't espouse terrorist methods?

Betty: *Well, as Bertie Russell himself said to me when he came to speak at the Spitalcliffe Women's Defence League and stayed round our house after – Now, that were a night! He says to me, 'Betty, take it from me: violence does not pay!'*

CM: Wise words, indeed!

Betty: *Soft ha'porth! We'll be needing more than hankies up our sleeves for next week's offensive on the D H S S. Don't forget to bring a Thermos and a can of spray-paint. Assemble at the bus station 4 a.m. sharp.*

S . P . L . A . F MANIFESTO

Sheffield Pensioners Liberation Army Faction

To secure for the elderly
by handbag or by brain
the full fruits of their longevity

A spectre is haunting Europe – and she's very, very old

No doubt you'll all be cognisant of the broad objectives of the Sheffield Pensioners Liberation Army Faction, but for those of you with your heads well buried in the sand I'd like to remind you of the main points of our manifesto.

WE DEMAND:

1 A 50% rise in pensions
2 Across-the-board increases in heating, clothing & death grants
3 Centralization of credit in the hands of the state
4 A minimum standard dying age of 87
5 Free bus travel for all pensioners regardless of race, creed, colour, gender or sexual proclivities
6 The immediate and unconditional release of Nelson Mandela

We have but one modest aim: to bring solace to the over-sixties and to train them into a fighting vanguard, prepared at a moment's notice to seize power – when history dictates.
SPLAF sees itself as breaking the mould of class-based politics. As everyone keeps saying these days, the class war is an outmoded concept – the age war is where it's at.

PENSIONERS ARISE!

YOU HAVE NOWT TO LOSE BUT YOUR PENSION BOOKS!

ALL POWER TO THE ELDERLY!

On Ageism

A Modern Plague?[1]

Ageism. It's a terrible thing. Not nice at all. And my comrades and I of SPLAF will not cease in our struggle to have this scourge obliterated from the face of the earth. Intolerance against others purely on the grounds of age is disgraceful, and I'll not tolerate it!

You may think me outspoken on this one, but it's a matter on which I feel strongly; just because some people are unfortunate enough to be under sixty is no reason to despise them.

Mind you, some of them ask for it. Only the other day our Tracey's youngest, Masher, was moaning and griping away at me about how fed up he were being stuck on the dole.

The apathy of kids these days! When I were their age you wouldn't catch me relying on state handouts. Oh, no! I'd be out there rioting, bringing government to its knees!

Of course it's the middle-aged I feel particularly sorry for. As Leon Trotsky himself said to me when he came to open the Spitalcliffe Gritshifters Union Summer Gala some time back. He said, 'Betty, I'd rather get an ice-pick stuck through my bonce than be married with flab and a mortgage, eating Flora and jogging!' Prophetic words as it happens, comrades, and profound with it.

But at least their sad state is merely temporary. Twerliedom will come to all in time, thank heaven, so long as they drive safely, go somewhere other than Sizewell for their holidays and make sure they carry a condom.

1. Reprinted from *The Little Red Pension Book*.

So, Pensioners of the World, next time a youngster offers to help you across the road, think for a moment, will you, about their predicament: poor kids. Brought up under Thatcherdom, forever fretting about how to pay off the Access bill they clocked up buying school-books, scared they're HIV positive because they once ate a runny boiled egg . . .

Comrades, think about their problems for a change! Then tell the condescending little twerps to shove off and leave you in peace.

On Coming Out

I'm sure most of my readers are already fully paid-up members of SPLAF, but it's just possible there may still be some wrinkled faces amongst you which we haven't yet seen at an AGM.

Of course, there are those who tell me they're too young to join, who strive to hide their crows-feet with cosmetics and cover their bald patches with pathetic wisps of hair. If there's one thing I can't stand, it's a closet pensioner.

For the rest of you, there's our Youth Wing. My live-in lover, Gavin, started that. Well, I say my lover. We've not been relating right well, lately. I mean, you'd have thought the man who founded the first-ever Husbands of Miners' Wives Support Group would know better, but there you are. If he's going to get mardy every time Doris and I indulge in a spot of political lesbianism, then stuff him, I say!

I'm sure you, dear reader, are made of sterner stuff. You wouldn't be reading a book like this if you weren't a hundred per cent committed to the pensioners' cause.

I know you'd not titter at the pensioners' plight, thank goodness. And why should you? It's your turn next, after all.

So, don't forget, Comrades. The Pensioners Liberation Army Faction needs you!

We've got nothing to lose. Better to set fire to yourself outside Number Ten than freeze to death alone.

The pension may not be worth owt, but converted into loose change and tied up in a sock it can give a riot cop what for.

DON'T VEGETATE – AGITATE!

The Bald Facts

- Number of pensioners in Britain today:
  10 million +

- Proportion of pensioners reliant on means-tested benefits:
  66%

- Proportion of women in total population over 75 yrs:
  68%

- Projected increase in population over 65 by 2001:
  4%

- Projected increase in population over 75 by 2001:
  28%

- Projected increase in population over 85 by 2001:
  50%

- Proportion of Twerlies preparing to SEIZE THE TIME:
  100%

- Source: SPLAFax Campaigners Factpack 1989.

Oldspeak
Some Basic Twerly Phraseology Explained

TWERLIES: The Radical Pensioners Movement takes its name from the gibes of its oppressors. The ageist powers-that-be have ordained that before 9 30 a.m. their hard-won bus passes are invalid. When pensioners attempt to board a bus before this randomly imposed time, bus crews mock them. They call them the 'Twerlies' as they proffer their passes and say, 'Sorry, pet. Am I too early?'

WRINKLIES/ BIDDIES/ DIRTY OLD MEN: In the face of such ageist terms of abuse, Twerlies counter through an oppositional vocabulary of their own, i.e.:
PEACHIES/ BUMFLUFFERS/ TWERPS: Young people
PROTO-TWERLIES/ MIDDLINGS/ FARTS: The middle-aged
BASILDON: Hell on earth. As 'Babylon' symbolizes to Rastafarians all that is bad about the British State, so the name of this new southern town is used to connote all things young and faceless.

CROSSING THE ROAD: Having sex. Whereas the young can talk freely about 'bonking' and 'gerrinalegover', societal intolerance of sexual activity amongst the old has driven the elderly to develop a secret code of richly descriptive euphemisms. 'Give us a hand crossing the road, love', 'Let's have a nice cup of hot chocolate' and 'popping down the shops' are some less obscene examples.

TWO: Twerly Liberation Organization
RPL: Revolutionary Pensioners League
LRP: League of Revolutionary Pensioners
WRPM: World Revolutionary Pensioners Movement
Just a few of the numerous but tiny sectarian factions and splinter-groups whose bitter intestinal in-fighting has so bedevilled the growth of the Elderly Movement.

WHITE PANTHERS: Make the Grey Panthers look like school kids and the Black Panthers like choirboys

TWIPNIGS: Two pensions, no grandchildren

WOOPIES: Well-off older people

JOLLIES: Jet-setting oldsters with lots of loot

GLAMS: Greying, leisured, affluent middle-aged

UPSHITS: Unglamorous pensioners suffering hardships intolerable today

ROTTERS: Rich old Tories

BIMPIES: Bloody irritating media people with nothing better to do with their time than dream up stupid little acronyms

A Word from the Typist

Dear Readers

Hello, there! My name's Agenda Overleaf and I'm terribly honoured to have been asked by my dear neighbour Betty to help out with the typing for her terrific little book. Well, as Betty quite rightly pointed out, it's criminal for Nicko's little word processor to just sit there idle all day while he's out at work and I'm knocking about the house going out of my mind with boredom, waiting to pop. (I'm thirty-two weeks now and banking on a Capricorn.)

Isn't Betty a marvel? I wish I had half her energy, I must say. But perhaps you're all like that up here, you pensioners? I wouldn't know. The thing is, I'm new to this part of the world. The thing is, actually, I'm from . . . forgive me . . . down there. You know, the Dreaded South!

Sorry.

We've had a friend of ours living here for years, actually. I remember when Josephine moved up from London. Well, I thought she was so brave. I admired her tremendously and she was always saying how marvellous it was being unemployed and things – being solid with the working classes. 'You must come up,' she kept saying. 'It's a great place, really. One is forever bumping into Arthur Scargill in the high street and the Peak District's just a cheap bus ride away . . .' Which sounded tempting but somehow we never got round to it, Nicko and I.

Isn't it awful of us, but we used to have this little sort of *in joke*, so that if anything really gloomy came up on the box, like a documentary on urban blight or nuclear winter or cervical smears, we'd look at each other, Nicko and I, and say 'Sheffield-esque' and change over.

And then little Sproglington made his presence known to us and . . . Well, I remember one night lying in the bath – like a

13

great fat pink walrus, quite frankly – in our hugely expensive tiny bedsit in Clapham and I suddenly had this sort of *experience* and I knew, I just knew, he was going to be a boy (at least I thought so) and that we were just destined somehow to bring up the kidlet somewhere just sort of . . . nicer. I don't know why, it just felt sort of *right for us*.

But I thought Nicko was pulling my leg when he first mentioned that he'd applied for a consultancy here with this new Youth Upthrust Public/Private Initiative Enterprise Sector they're setting up. I only came up with him for a lark on the day of his interview and met up with Josephine after all this time and had a look around and . . .

Well! I suppose I'd always imagined it as all sort of grey and blighted. But it was fine. I mean fine. Really. That new arcade, the parks . . . Really, seriously, fine.

And there's Jos (as she calls herself these days, thank you very much), living in this enormous house not ten minutes from the city centre with a garden, I ask you, which would cost a small fortune, I mean, really, in London. And she's working part-time, for god's sake, for some trendy arts thing and making all these snidy remarks about southern affluence which takes the biscuit, rather, considering she'd need to gross god knows how many umpteen thou in London to live that kind of life-style. And up here they still have a National Health and social services and council-subsidized Bertolucci seasons and everything. Street credibility and a spare room – I could have killed her!

So, we sold our little bedsit in Clapham. Bought a street up here. And we love it here, really we do. We love it. Nicko too, he does love it. Thinks it super. We feel we've always lived here and, anyway, house prices are rocketing here now and we can always move back down south when Nicko's mummy dies. Oh, how awful! God forbid. Not that we'd *want* to but we could, couldn't we, if for some weird reason we ever did?

And our neighbours are so marvellously down to earth up here, marvellously gritty sort of thing, not a bit stuck up. We've got Betty on one side, of course, and the architect in the house next-but-one swears like a trooper at his kids and you should see his idea of a smart business suit! A far cry from London, I can tell you.

And the whole city's so steeped. So steeped in this marvellous Socialist Tradition. Which is no problem for me because I know it sounds horribly naff to say so these days but there's nothing wrong in my book with caring for the poor and shabby.

Personally, I don't care what people say. I can't stand that Thatcher woman and I don't care who knows it. Which isn't to say she's not got guts and, let's face it, the trade unions had it coming, didn't they? But there are limits.

So I'm really one hundred and one per cent behind you marvellous pensioners *doing your thing* like this, if you'll pardon the expression.

And I think it's terribly sad. You must all be so upset about it. Tragic. Socialism dying like that.

Sorry.

Yours,
Agenda

SPLAF Central Committee

1 ELIZABETH SPITAL: Gen. Sec., Collective Member-in-Chief and Hon. President
2 DORIS BENDIBUS: Aide to Gen. Sec.
3 ARNOLD BENDIBUS: Treasurer, husb. of aide to Gen. Sec.
4 VERA TOTLEY: Careerist Woopy infiltrator. Mind you, she can organize a mean Bring and Buy sale when she's in the mood.

ASSOCIATE MEMBERS

1 AGENDA OVERLEAF: Neighbour of Gen. Sec., daughter of local government clerk, voluntary(ish) personal sec. of Gen. Sec.
2 GAVIN YOUNGPERSON: Chair of our Youth Wing. Changed his name by deed poll as symbolic act of contrition for subconscious ageism. Mind you, now he's pushing forty, perhaps he should change it back again to Pratt.
3 ROSA EGHAM NÉE SPITAL: Daughter of civil servant and reactionary lackey. Only made her a member to get up her nose.
4 DOCTOR STANLEY NETHEREDGE: Amateur New Gerontologist and Chief of SPLAF Think-Tank.

HONORARY MEMBERS

1 KARL MARX: Old friend and mentor of Gen. Sec. Ooh, that ticklish beard!
2 JAMES STEWART: Gen. Sec. always fancied him rotten.
3 LEN MURRAY: Another of the Gen. Sec's heroes.

4 IAN McCASKILL: More beefcake.

5 MRS GANDHI: Admittedly never a fully paid-up member of SPLAF, but as we're still unfortunately an all-white organization, despite our membership drive, we thought we'd put her in.

6 BILLIE HOLLIDAY: And having just one black member smacked of tokenism.

7 SAMANTHA FOX: The man from Penguin says that having a young topless model in the book somewhere could help to boost sales no end.

CM: Betty Spital, radical, visionary, veteran campaigner, the story of your life has been played out against the dramatic canvas of many of the great political events of this turbulent century.

Betty: *Oh, aye?*

CM: To help us set your personal crusade in its correct socio-historical context, would you mind terribly if I were to ask how old you are exactly?

Betty: *Of course, there are them as would say that question was highly offensive, but I don't agree. It's no ruder than me asking you for the precise dimensions of your private parts.*

CM: Moving on . . . In your time you've mingled with many of the major thinkers and activists of the age. Are there any particular heroes that stand out?

Betty: *Not especially.*

CM: Not even one?

Betty: *Michael was a one.*

CM: Michael . . . Foot? Gorbachev? Jackson?

Betty: *Little Micky Matlock, him as played sax for the Spitalclif-*
fettes. A lovely pair of lips he had.

CM: Really?

Betty: *Nice bum, too.*

CM: Yes . . Take us back in time, if you will, to your childhood
days. It must have been a terrible struggle for you then . . .

Betty: *Fags was cheaper then, mind.*

CM: Yes, but the exploitation, the poverty, the drink . . .

Betty: *Thank you, dearie, don't mind if I do.*

ALL MY OWN TEETH
The Memoirs of Betty Spital

Part I
The Formative Years

Chapter 1
Reminiscences of Old Spitalcliffe

I'm a Sheffielder born and bred, me. I could tell you some tales about the old days. They've knocked down Spitalcliffe where I were born years back. Good thing, too. It were such a slum that you couldn't move for academics researching urban decay.

The lot of us were rehoused on the flats, eventually. They're world famous now. We've had people come from all over to look at the graffiti art. Then they commit suicide by jumping off the top. I don't know why. They only end up at the bottom in a great pile of dogs' doings, not a scratch on 'em.

There's not many as believe us old folk when we say we can remember a time before fast-food joints, discount jeans shops and clip-together DIY superstores. Hard times, but still life had its pleasures. We kids slept nine or ten in a bed – when our folks were out and we fancied an orgy.

But there were some characters: Scabby Dolly Fargate had a shop selling dandelion, burdock and backstreet abortions. Old Leggy Furnival, he sold leeches door-to-door, a sort of precursor of BUPA, really.

My Dad were a grit shifter at Thwitelworks. Lugged sacks of old grot to a barge on the River Sheff. Then they'd send it for reprocessing into beefburgers down its tributary, the Little Sheff.

Of course we all talked proper dialect in them days. I remember our Dad'd say to us, 'Ee, thar's mardy gobsmacked thy coil hoil, chuff me old mank!' No one understood a word he said, even then. Well, I call him our dad. Mam being a great proponent of free love and notoriously absent-minded, she were never too

sure which one of the Spitalcliffe Workers' Union Committee it were on that particular night.

Ours was an intensely political household. We kids were sent to a Socialist Sunday School so as we could learn the precepts of Marxism and our mam and dad could have it away in the parlour in peace.

The kitchen became meeting-place for many local radical organizations: the Socialist League, the Clarion Choir, the Guild of Co-operative Womenfolk and Allied Polytechnic Lecturers, members of the Anti-War Movement, the End Imperialism Now Committee, and the Sheffield and District Glottal Stop Preservation Society. It got so bad eventually, we kids couldn't ask to be excused without the demand getting minuted and proposed as a motion at the AGM.

Robert Tressell, the novelist, was a very close friend of mother's. The Ragged-Trousered Philanderer we called him. But he was a great favourite with us kids.

23

We loved it when he entertained us with his tricks, like fishing two slices of granary out of his pocket and declaring, 'This sandwich, children, is a bit like life under the capitalist system!'

'Why?' we inquired eagerly, gathering around him, our young eyes bright with anticipation. 'Is it because it represents the raw materials which exist naturally in and on the earth for all, but which the bosses have seized and say they own, setting us to work chopping the bread into squares for which they pay us pennies, which we must then give back to them to buy those raw materials we need to feed and clothe ourselves, making them a pile of money and us paupers?'

'Nope,' he'd say, pulling back the top slice of bread to reveal a filling of foul-smelling brown stuff. 'Because the more bread you've got, the less shit you eat!' And he'd laugh uproariously and take a huge mouthful.

A good socialist, but stark-staring bonkers.

Karl Marx came to our house one Christmas, I remember. We kids all had to sit on his knee and tell him what we wanted in our stockings come the revolution.

Of an evening we'd sit round the fire and he'd read to us from this book he were working on. *Das Kapital* it were called. Well, I got bored. I were only a nipper at the time, remember. 'Mister Marx,' I said to him, 'not another bloody guidebook to London! Why don't you write summat about class and oppression?'

'*Meine kleine schpitalischgefreund,*' he said, 'you could be on to something there!'

Didn't even get a flaming acknowledgement.

We were brought up according to strict Marxist-Spitalist childcare methods: they locked us in the cellar till history dictated that we arose.

Schooling was very basic. Just the three 'R's': reading, riting and rioting. The school motto was *Protestatem et Survivibus* and it was the first place in the world to have Peace Studies as an essential subject of the core curriculum; one afternoon per week they'd put sticking-plaster over our mouths and go off to sleep.

The discipline there stood me in good stead for adult life, mind.

Well, if kiddies spend their childhood being bullied, shouted at and beaten black and blue, then it does make their lifelong suffering under the cruel tyranny of capitalist patriarchy seem a doddle in comparison.

The bosses tried to grind us down, but we never lost our sense of pride. When Queen Victoria came to Sheffield they polished our clogs and cleaned our nits up special like. We may have been poor, but, by God, we were picturesque.

No video nasties then; we made our own entertainment. When we wanted a thrill we'd go out to the suburbs and chuck bricks at toffs.

Those were the days, eh?

Bloody miserable.

The Everytwerly Guide to Grandchildcare

It is a commonly held belief that every woman over retirement age longs with all her heart to see offspring producing babies in their turn, spreading the fresh, joyous sound of children's laughter like sunshine into the drab and dreary existences of their lonely withered old folk. When the fact is, that having finally got the brats off your hands, the last thing you want is to have your peace wrecked yet again by wailing, puking infants.

However, we do have a duty as grandparents to help out the young. As my friend Vera Totley always says, 'Men hit women, women hit kids, kids take it out on the elderly.' And the best way of ending this tragic spiral of violence is to nip it in the bud by ganging up with the kids against their parents.

What's more, with patience and care, you can help to mould the new generation into a useful little army of helpers – unpaid home helps for yourself – and invaluable undercover agents in the cold war against the middle-aged.

The following tips, if applied with thought and sensitivity, should prove invaluable in handling the challenges of grandparenthood.

ANTE-NATAL DEPRESSION: It is not uncommon for Twerlies to feel depressed immediately before the birth of their first grandchild. This is nothing to feel ashamed of. The thought of hours of unpaid childminding to come is a daunting prospect.

BOTTLE-FEEDING: Drown your sorrows in Guinness, gin or whatever other mind-expanding beverages you have to hand. Grandchildren are here to stay, worse luck, and the ordeal ahead is best considered through a good alcoholic haze.

CHANGES TO SURROUNDINGS: Before baby's first visit be sure to place fragile ornaments and electrical appliances at a height where they can easily be reached by young hands. This establishes firmly to the parents that your personal space is your own, and not a free crèche for their little horrors whenever your daughter wants a few hours off to further her career as a noxious Yuppie or to have it off with the new boyfriend.

DISCIPLINE: Corporal punishment is barbaric and inhumane, and a complete waste of energy for people who may no longer be running at full strength. Admit it, you don't pack the same punch you used to. Anyway, as any teacher will tell you, mental cruelty can be far more effective.

EDUCATION: Training your grandchild in the facts of life is vital, but the heavy-handed approach is not recommended. Substituting *The Complete Works of Engels* for *Spot's First Walk* as bedtime reading may do more harm than good; the trick is to see the world with the young child's innocent vision – and then seek to subvert it.

Introduce interesting talking-points like 'Why does Santa wear red?'; play imaginative games like 'I Spy with My Little Eye Encroachments by the State into the Liberty of the Individual'; invent amusing stories equating parents with military dictators, cabinet ministers and suchlike. And, remember, don't expect instant results; grandchildren of mine have shown little to no interest in the guerrilla techniques of Che Guevara before their fourth birthday, if not even later.

FITS AND VOMITING: Simulation of these when grandchildren or their parents dare to challenge your word can be useful for: GUILT (*see next tip*).

GUILT (INDUCTION OF EARLY IN THE YOUNG): This is crucial. Don't forget, however, that even old standards like, 'Don't you move a muscle, pet. I'll just risk heart seizure by doing it myself!' may seem corny to you, but work a treat on innocent young ones.

HEARING DIFFICULTIES: Learn from the child's ability to refuse to hear unwanted commands.

IMAGINATION: Children have lots of it, let it run riot. Parents have less, help it develop through story-telling. 'Once upon a time there was a daddy who cheated on his wife . . .' is a good opener. See the speed with which even the most sock-brained father will rush to invent another story of his own. And why not stretch your own powers by inventing some juicy tales of the 'Let me tell you about the time when your mummy was a very naughty girl . . .' variety?

JEALOUSY: You can't be blamed for feeling jealous that the new arrival is hogging all the limelight. Take every opportunity you can to act crotchety and cussed. For example, this could be the perfect time to develop a tricky new medical complaint necessitating much attention from your immediate family.

KARL MARX: *see under* MOTHER'S MILK (to be imbibed with).

LIPSTICK: Always keep a plentiful supply of the bright pink, highly scented brands and apply liberally before visits. Should over-excited youngsters turn a mite trying during your stay, simply smile, purse your lips and whisper, 'Pack in that racket sharpish, brats, or I'll give you such a smacking kiss beddy-byes later, you'll be scraping this muck of your chops for months to come!' That should do the trick.

MASTURBATION: Not in front of the children.

MOTHER'S MILK: Come to think of it, Jenny Marx preferred bottle to breast. Her recipe was one part Schnapps to two parts Formula: good for gripe, wind and alienation.

NAPPY-CHANGING: Fastening one of these new-style disposable paper nappies is a doddle. Don't let your children realize you can do it. Insist that they can't teach an old dog new tricks.

ODOURS: Toilet-training is not difficult either; at the first whiff to emanate from your grandchild's nappy, hand him/her/it firmly back to the parent with the simple command: 'Go!'

PRESENTS: Christmas and birthdays are major events in the lives of tots and provide ample opportunity for grandparental interference. Remember, grandchildren and their parents will be duty-bound to show gratitude whatever rubbish you give them. Whether you go for the more conventional line of unhousetrained puppies, drum-kits, stink bombs, or strange-looking things made of raffia and matchboxes, or take a more radical approach with Urban Guerrilla Kits for Charmaine and a 'My Little Hooligan' doll for Darryl depends entirely on what you consider will be most effective in getting up the nose of whoever (child or adult) you most want to annoy at the time.

QUESTIONS: 'Because I say so' has been discredited recently as a fitting reply to youthful interrogation. However, it seems to me quite adequate in defining the power relationship to be instilled between the elderly and the inquisitive young.

RESPECT FOR THE OLD: This cannot be forced, however. Only by setting a good example can you hope to gain the admiration of young children. Impress them with your skill at getting your own way, cheating at cards, expertise with a catapult, etc.

SHARING CHILDCARE: Of course, parents themselves should always be urged – nay, forced – to divide childcare duties 50/50. My own son-in-law claimed he had far too much on his plate at work to 'help out' our Rosa at home. It only took a couple of phone calls to his boss to get him sacked, and now he's far more compliant.

On the other hand, the last thing grandparents want is to be lumbered with any tiresome responsibilities themselves. Avoid habit-forming tendencies such as regular baby-sitting. Keeping the parents constantly on their toes is an absolute must.

TREATS AND SPOILING: The importance of spoiling the young grandchild cannot be over-emphasized. Plying them with presents and sweets at an early age is crucial if you wish to persuade them to connive on your behalf later. Items banned by parents (tooth-rotting chew bars, E-chemical-enriched soft drinks, reading matter of a nature deemed unsuitable for their little dears) are a particularly useful addition to any granny's armoury.

URINE: Nothing to do with you, whatsoever.

VERA TOTLEY: A dear friend of mine had six grandchildren at the last count, all of them besotted with her. They are always round her flat cleaning and cooking, and immediately informed her when their dad mentioned that perhaps she should be 'packed off' to a council home. Under their granny's instructions, they aided her campaign of non-co-operation by spreading it round school that 'daddy's planning to bump off granny Vera and pretend she's gone away'.

WILFULNESS: Both young and old have a part to play in eradicating this ugly tendency in the middle-aged.

X-RATED FILMS: If, through following the advice above, you manage successfully to steer your grandchild through the perils of infancy to see them blossom into a pleasingly rebellious adolescent, confirm the bond of complicity by taking him/her/it to the cinema for a treat.

Watch their sweet little faces light up as you lead them, not to

The Sound of Music, as their parents believe, but to whatever prurient shocker their schoolmates are currently most desperate to feast their eyes on. Feel their disappointment as you clamp your hand firmly over their eyes for what you call the 'mucky bits'. Hear them swear to do your bidding evermore as they bargain to secure an eyeful of the exploitative poppycock you are watching.

YELLING, WHINING, SCREAMING, SCRATCHING, BITING: All perfectly valid forms of resistance against oppression. We can all learn a thing or two from our nappy-bound comrades on this score.

ZZZZ, SLEEP, GETTING THEM OFF TO: If, by any chance, your offspring should manage to con you into allowing their brats to stay with you overnight, this is your chance to have some fun trying out all those little short-cuts and old wives' tales you never dared risk when you were a caring and responsible mother. Try a spot of gin in baby's bottle, perhaps, rubbing a hot onion in its ear, dosing it with a brew of nettle and garlic, or simply leaving it to howl for hours in a soggy nappy. If challenged, simply say, 'Well, that's how we always used to do it in my day, dear. Perhaps times have changed.'

'Chaos, Quarks, Quacks and Quids'

The New Gerontology

by Dr Stanley Netheredge © 1989

To date, gerontologists such as myself (those embarked upon the scientific study of the processes of growing old), whilst amassing a large and rapidly growing volume of significant and informative data concerning what we know of as age, have so far taken as the basis of their work certain key and somewhat limiting assumptions which can be succinctly summarized thus: people grow older and frailer and eventually die.

However, it is my strongly held belief that certain recent advances in the field of learning, advances which embrace disciplines as far apart as particle physics and meteorology, have dramatic implications for the future development of this rapidly growing branch of socio-medical thought.

In this paper I will offer a concise explication of some of the major current intellectual trends in the gerontological arena, basing my words in part on the trail-blazing research of my colleague Professor Schwarzkopf, author of *Aufgerripen und die Ganzege-krinklich* (Munich, 1987).

Up to now our societal view of the human lifespan has been seen to follow the pattern illustrated in Fig. 1.

In this traditional linear model old age is associated with decay, dependency and disengagement from social activity. Expressions in common parlance such as 'autumn years', 'past his prime' and 'in her dotage' reinforce this essentially negative picture.

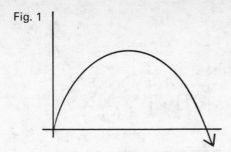

Fig. 1

But if we look at the work of those new physicists, mathematicians *et al.*, who so convincingly postulate that many of our most fundamental assumptions about the nature of time and matter are utterly fallacious, that, far from living in an ordered universe governed by constant scientific laws and proven fact, we actually inhabit a chaotic infinity of black holes, random quarks, lumps of theoretical anti-matter and naked singularities in which time, space, dead cats and thought may, or may not, be one and the same, in which, according to Von Alzheimer's famous dictum 'To be is not to be, probably', then the prospects for new theories concerning the nature of life look up no end.

For instance, if we bring to the data concerned with human lifespan the rule associated with the Mangelbrat set, i.e., that $z \rightarrow z? + c$, in which c is the complex number corresponding to the point being tested and $\rightarrow$ is taken to represent the sum of all the funny little symbols I can make on my word processor, and if we bifurculate the resulting pectorals and periodicize them, we find a very different picture of the human life cycle begins to emerge, looking something like this:

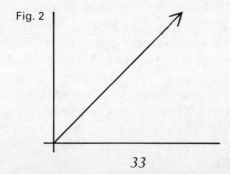

Fig. 2

Or this:

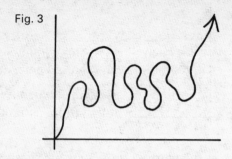

Fig. 3

Or, come to think of it, even this:

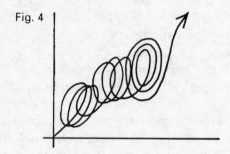

Fig. 4

Now to the lay person, all this may seem somewhat daunting. It need hardly be said that this is precisely the point. But whereas it is hardly likely to be of interest to the average pensioner to know that the apparently random time delay between outbreaks of the twinges he experiences in his back, if plotted precisely and fed through my lap-top, produces a rather beautiful swirly sort of shape reminiscent of cumulus cloud formations and old psychedelic record sleeves, once we add to such a discovery a holistic appreciation of Professor White's theory of the therapeutic effects of imaginative pretence: 'We are What We are Convinced We are', a far more practical use for this observation starts to appear.

For it is now not unjustifiable to construct from the data a radically new pattern charting the course of the individual human life (*see* Table 1):

Table I Phases of development of the average human being

Pre-birth: Conception, early stages of biological development, kicking and making mother feel sick, looking like an aborted chicken.

Birth–11 years: Acquisition of basic skills in locomotion, perception, parent irritation, assimilation of cultural characteristics, i.e., ageism, sexism, racism, etc.

Adolescence: Acquisition of spots, trendy clothes, dirty mind.

21–50: Acquisition of adult roles: mortgages, brats, hypertension, tedious career ambitions, irritating little habits, peak years for boringness.

50–65: Pre-retirement. Peak years for smug sense of achievement in career, unless made redundant. Acquisition of time to self, now brats off hands.

65 onwards: Consolidation of wisdom, peak years for athletic, artistic, political, scientific and intellectual achievement, maximum sexual performance, acquisition of overwhelming sense of well-being and correct ideological perspective.

Death: Peaked.

And so, whereas for most people the process of human ageing is associated with inevitable decline, New Gerontologists prefer to see it as a highly flexible concept covering an infinity of variables liable at any time to speed up, reverse, turn somersaults or vanish completely, but which we generally represent to old people as an ever-rising line, peaking at the top.

Why? *Because research proves categorically that a majority of the elderly population would rather see it that way and are prepared to pay considerable sums in order to be persuaded this is so.*

Which leads me, aptly enough, to my conclusion. If we return to the origins of the word gerontology, we find it comes from the Greek 'geron', meaning old, mature, wise, beyond reproach and 'ology' meaning you can write books about it, run evening classes in it, appear on TV and radio talking about it – and possibly end up as professor of it, till death or early retirement, in some nice cosy university somewhere. The pertinence of this fact to pensioners seeking to bring down the Government and/or find easy means of income generation to help supplement their measly state pensions will, I have no doubt, be crystal clear.

This paper was delivered by Dr Stanley Netheredge, self-employed gerontological consultant, at a SPLAF seminar on 'How to Survive on a Pension'. Other speakers included a High Court judge, several peers of the realm and a carpark attendant.   [Ed.]

Whither the Elderly?
Programme for a SPLAF Dayschool

SEMINARS

9.30   Dying as a Campaigning Tool

10.30   Tea and Biscuits

11.00   The Pensioner's Role in the Nuclear Family and Beyond

12.30   **LUNCHEON**
(during which Mrs Bendibus will be showing her slides of ·
SPLAF's recent Sellafield outing)

1.30   **WORKSHOPS**
Reclaiming Senility (Please wear loose clothing)
Flower Arrangement (Marxist-Spitalist)

3.00   **VIDEO**
It weren't 'Arf Itchy
Film by the Community History Workshop in which 150 old
people from all walks of life reminisce about life before soft
toilet paper.

4.00   **PLENARY**
'Whither next?'

5.00   **DEPART**

CM: Ms Spital, your collection of thoughts and speeches covers a huge plethora of contemporary issues making truly profound insights into . . .

Betty: *Beg pardon?*

CM: You must have done a lot of public speaking in your time.

Betty: *Oh, aye. Recently I've addressed the Women's Institute, the TUC, the Confederation of British Industry, all the party conferences – even the little squitty ones – on ageism and what have you. I've spoken in local Council meetings, in Parliament, in the American Senate, on live television discussions . . .*

CM: Good gracious!

Betty: *They never listen mind.*

CM: But surely it's an honour in itself to have been invited to speak to so many important bodies?

Betty: *Oh, I don't get invited. I just sneak in the back way, wait for a lull in proceedings and then let 'em have it: 'UP WITH THE PENSION, GRANNYF***ERS!'*

On That Other Great British Female Political Figure of Pensionable Age

I may not agree with everything Margaret Thatcher has said or done, but even a dyed-in-the-wool Socialist such as myself has to admire her tremendous guts and determination. Then, again, *I* had a soft spot for Stalin.

But, as I travel this land, I can't help but be impressed by the evidence of the new attitude of get-up-and-go that her Enterprise Culture has managed to engender in ordinary folk. Like our plucky lads in the prisons, entirely off their own bats, organizing riots. Or our Scottish comrades having the spunk to tear up their Poll Tax forms.

I know Margaret's Aunt Elsie very well; she's heavily involved in the Grantham Grannies, an Anarcho-Feminist cell of ours. But, to be frank, I don't think her and her niece see entirely eye to eye. Mind you, Elsie swears blind that 'her Mags' is an old softy underneath that nannyish, battle-axe exterior.

Which was a disappointment to me. Myself, I've always harboured a secret dream of all that stubborn, philistine, narrow-minded, ruthless megalomania being harnessed somehow to the forces of Good. We've been looking for someone like that to be our Membership Secretary for years.

On the Monarchy

If she'd ever had to lift a finger to change a nappy or dab Dettol on a grazed knee or cook sausage, egg and chips for ten six-year-old Brownies, it might be different, but in these liberated days for a woman in her position to publicly define herself merely in terms of her domestic role as the Queen's Mother seems to me frankly contemptible.

She must be terribly disappointed about how the kiddies turned out, though. Hardly a day goes by without one of them getting their names plastered across the front pages of the tabloids. When will they learn to behave?

That pinko-revisionist Charles is the worst with his pseudo-populist, philistine attitude to architecture. What does he know about life in a tower block? Or perhaps people urinate in the lifts where he lives.

No, I don't hold with royalty, me. I know a lot of old people dote on them, and think they do a damn fine job for this country, shaking hands and having babies all the while, just to keep us amused.

But we can't always be pandering to our senile fringe.

On the Co-operative Ideal

I were in the Spitalfoot Co-op some time back, waiting in the queue for taramasalata behind the usual line of social workers. All that sort bank at the Co-op, making their stand against capitalist profiteering by supporting tight-fistedness and crass inefficiency.

I finished my shopping and I were just off to take part in the SPLAF-sponsored streak against hypothermia when this hand descended on my shoulder. Now, the thing is, I'd been liberating teabags for our next AGM, so I did what I always do in such circumstances – followed our guidelines on Acting Senile. We have workshops on this at our SPLAF drop-in centre, if anyone's interested. I turned to the young gentleman who'd grabbed me and muttered, 'Oh, dearie me. Have I done summat wrong, love? My mind's not what it was since the mugging.' But he wasn't fooled.

So next I used a tip from our Self-Defence Course: I kicked him sharply in the testicles and made for the exit. He were too quick for me.

Next tactic: the Embarrassing Scene. 'Thug!' I shouted. 'Bully! Thief! Pervert!' You know, not a soul turned a hair! What's happened to human compassion in this consumerist society? That's what I'd like to know.

And then I bit him.

'Let go of me! I patronized this museum of a shop when there was still time to have you aborted!'

Comrades, I told this young whelp a thing or two about the history of the Co-operative Movement. I remember when this building were first opened, when Pablo Picasso himself stood on the steps between Haberdashery and Bedding and scribbled doves of peace on the people's waterproof over-jackets.

'Betty,' Pablo said to me, 'there will come a day when the workers will share of the fruits of their labour and this shop shall stock more than tasteless plain biscuits, when working women of Sheffield will no longer have to queue for hours to buy ugly wrought-iron telephone tables, when society shall truly be caring and sharing!'

'Pablo,' I said to him, 'I hope I live to see that great day.'

Oh, yes. I told this management hireling a thing or two. But it cut no ice. What was a poor, defenceless old woman like me to do? I admit it, I grovelled. I pleaded for pity. Took some persuading, but he let me off in the end. He took back the teabags, mind.

I walked home through the chill streets of Spitalcliffe, a lonely old lady in a harsh, heartless world. Back at my flat I brewed up a cup of hot water.

Fire-damaged stock (asparagus tips, liqueurs and other luxury produce), courtesy of the Spitalfoot Co-op, available free to members, following the recent unfortunate conflagration. Contact B. Spital for further details.

On Humour

People are always saying to me – 'Betty,' they say, 'cheer up. It may never happen. Life has its trials, but you've got to laugh sometimes, haven't you!'

Bollocks. Why don't people ever turn to me and say, 'Betty, life has its humorous moments, but you've got to rise up in armed revolt against state corruption sometimes'? Eh? That's what I'd like to know.

Then again, fun's not as funny as it was in my day. Frederick Engels. Now he *was* a comedian. He used to tell this hilarious story about the Englishman, the Irishman, the Scotsman and the degrading effect of colonialism on the working class . . .

It was the way he told 'em, mind.

Sex, Drugs and Rock 'n' Roll

Popular Culture and Media Images of Sexuality, a Marxist-Spitalist Intervention

Young people today think rock music was invented by Michael Jackson! As lead singer with SPLAF's own little musical ensemble, Betty and the Death Grants,[1] I keep telling them it's nothing new. My old friend Lennon did it all in his day! And then, again, the Beatles owed a great debt to George Formby.

Middle-aged youth workers think they invented drugs. All that carry-on about Marryjiuana and Acid Rain and such. My old Billy was injecting himself with dandelion and burdock before they were born! And you wouldn't catch him pretending he'd caught the flu. They may have been spaced-out junkies then, but, by gum, they were proud! Mind you, old Billy did die before he were twelve, come to think of it.

It's the attitude to sex these days I can't do with. These poor girlies, still at school, wearing make up, dolling themselves up in mini-skirts and all sorts, flirting with spotty little boys, getting pregnant before they've reached puberty. It shocks me – really it does.

As I was telling the Sheffield Pensioners Liberation Army Faction's Family Values Sub-Committee the other day. 'Girls,' I said, 'when I were young it were different. We girls knew our place in society. When I fancied a fuck I'd just collar a comrade,

---

1. Available soon: the CD remix of Betty and the Death Grants' 'Let's Dance (and Bring About the Overthrow of Western Capitalism)', Progress Records and Tapes, No. OAP 784.

betty
and the
deathgrants

TWERLYPHONE

mono

tell him how I liked it, and if he came before I did I'd have him expelled from the party at the next AGM for reformist tendencies.'

On Tolerance

You've got to be tolerant. At my age you learn to be. We've got to show a bit of common decency.

I was talking to Jackie Hackenthorpe the other week about her husband, Bill. She says, 'Betty, he comes in drunk, does nowt around the house, abuses me summat rotten when he's had a few.'

I says to her, 'Now, Jackie, be fair. Working men have enough on their plate what with alienation and womb-envy and the crisis of capitalism. Jackie,' I said, 'don't be too harsh on him. You can't go and leave him, smash his car up and set fire to his pigeon loft – not till the divorce is through!'

Of course, there are limits. When our Michael[1] got himself elected on to Council,[2] I were that proud. I thought, he'll make the Commons yet, that boy. I'll show that Hattersley woman, mouthing off about her precious Roy. It was our Michael as got the resolution through demanding large-print Lenin to be introduced at Central Library.

So I put a brave face on it when they threatened to bar him from public office, repossess his house and declare him bankrupt over that rate-capping palaver.

---

1. Not in fact flesh and blood relations but Betty's godson, M. Bendibus, who for a time she unofficially adopted in preference to her own child.

2. SPLAF have been staunch, though not uncritical, supporters of municipal Socialism for many years. A SPLAF-organized 'Council Carnival', at the time of the Rate-capping Campaign, was to have involved a huge procession of cleaners, dinner ladies, refuse collection vans, etc., filing past the Town Hall, and a million library books laid out like dominoes to spell WE LOVE SHEFFIELD! But the event was called off at the last minute after Betty's bitter dispute with Sheffield Libraries over non-payment of fines over the past half-century.

[Ed.]

Mind you, when he voted to set a legal rate, I had to tell him: *Show your Face Round Here Again, You Defeatist Flaming Traitor, and I'll Kick Your Chuffing Head In!* Someone had to say it.

On the Role of the Whist Drive in Arresting Inner-City Decay

For those as don't know – and there's not many as do yet, frankly – I think I can now safely reveal to you that Sheffield looks well in line to be the venue for the 1992 International Elderly Olympics.

We in SPLAF are very excited about this development, as it's a splendid chance to put the city on the world map in terms of international pensioners sports. It's also an opportunity to attract a great deal of investment to the city in the form of sponsorship from sportswear and thermal underwear manufacturers, etc. Furthermore, it's clearly in line with the Government's overall policy of turning the entire North of England into an enormous leisure complex by the year two thousand.

Despite impressive bids from New York, Edinburgh, Moscow and Lytham St Annes, our position looks strong for several reasons:

1 Our pedestrian underpasses can be easily redeveloped and utilized as wheelchair-racing stadia.
2 Condensation problems in our council blocks make them ripe for transformation into shower facilities for competitors.
3 The high incidence of youth unemployment in the city has created an enormous pool of youngsters on the streets available to help across busy roads the large numbers of elderly visitors these prestigious games will attract.
4 The number of pensioners and the prevailing economic conditions in the city mean that Sheffield leads the world in such

athletic events for the elderly as Long Distance Queue-Standing. You may not be aware that the current queue-standing World Champion is a Spitalcliffe resident. Eric Moorfoot stood in a 400-metre queue for a staggering twenty-four hours whilst awaiting information about his Housing Benefit Claim.

Perhaps most crucial of all are the long-term links established with our Eastern-bloc colleagues on the International Games Selection Committee. So, sucks to you, Tory mockers of twinning!

Now then, I'm sure there are those among you who may disapprove of such measures as clearing council high-rise blocks of their young tenants to turn them into viewing platforms for spectators of the Zimmerframe Marathon, which will be a focal point for the Games. Others may be dismayed at the thought of pedestrian precincts being turfed over to create an Olympic-sized bowling-green. Perhaps you feel the Crucible Theatre is better used for snooker than whist drives.

But to such doubters I say we old folk can no longer afford to live in the past. With cuts and privatization so rampant, our only hope of receiving decent provision in future is to get our impending senility sponsored sharpish by the high street chain-stores.

I have a dream, comrades, of South Yorkshire at the forefront of investment in the growing nostalgia-boom, transforming this region into an enormous industrial museum and theme park, and marketing it as a tourist resort for tomorrow's designer-pensioner from down South.

Marxist-Spitalism must move with the times, and if style is where it's at then we must cut our packamacs accordingly.

On Cruelty to Animals and the Overwhelming Desire to Inflict It

Better be a whale than an old woman these days.

On Hypothermia

As I said to my neighbour Arnold Bendibus when he popped round our house the other week – 'Arnold,' I said, 'Arnold, your searching tongue drives my yearning body to a wild frenzy of burning joy. Our passion may be but temporary, yet in its brevity still it illumines the very depths of me.'

Well, since they put up the bus fares, we Twerlies need all the cheap entertainment we can get, and sex is the best preventative for hypothermia I've come across. Bar none.

On the Irish Problem

Well, that one's a doddle. SPLAF has an infallible method for bringing lasting and just peace to the North, ending bloodlessly the terrible troubles that have bedevilled the Irish for so long. The idea is so simple I can't think why no one else thought of it long since. It was Arnold's cousin Kathleen who came up with the idea.

'Betty,' she said to me, 'X X!'

Penguin Books regret that Government Anti-Terrorist legislation makes it an offence to print the direct speech of anyone whose neighbour's son's best friend was once rumoured to have chalked UP THE IRA on the wall of a public convenience in licensed premises.

ALL MY OWN TEETH

The Memoirs of Betty Spital

Part II
Slices from the Breadbin of History

Including extracts from the Collected Writings of Doris and Arnold Bendibus

Chapter 2
A Sapling in the Groves of Academe

When you consider my somewhat scant academic qualifications up to that point (GCSE Applied Buffing, grade C), you will realize what a miracle it was for a girl of my humble origins to find herself wending her way to Cambridge, city of glittering spires, honey sandwiches and quaint little punts.

Well, I dozed off on the train from Barnsley and woke up just outside Newmarket. Couldn't afford the fare home. So it was that I mingled with the underwear of intellectual giants; I got a job as a 'bedder' at one of the colleges. The things I don't know about Sir Arthur Quiller-Couch's understains could be written on the back of a pair of yellow Y-fronts.

I came to mix with a somewhat bohemian crowd. We thought ourselves very daring as we smoked cigarettes and consumed champagne and strawberries, snorted cocaine and sunbathed naked on the banks of the Cam, planning anarchist bomb outrages in those halcyon days. How naive we all were!

I had men friends then, of course, but in those days there was no hanky-panky. Foreplay before marriage was unthinkable. It was just 'wham bam, thank you, ma'm and have you ever considered a career in the secret service?'

Did wonders for my consciousness. In fact it was whilst scrubbing stubborn white spots off the sheets of a budding captain of industry that I resolved to pull myself up by my own bra straps and get myself an education.

The only educational opening available at that time to a young girl of my background in such a bastion of male supremacy was, to put it bluntly, between one's blue stockings. I worked out my own timetable, pinpointing all the brightest undergraduates in the subjects which most interested me, then bedded them systematically, picking their wits for titbits of knowledge over post-coital ciggies.

And so I'm an expert at physics (all talk and no action), have a frankly bizarre view of mathematics and know all the classics backwards (but sadly not the right way round). My knowledge of politics is deep and probing and to this day the very word geography brings me up in goose bumps.

My little coterie included Binky (soon to become Lord Admiral of the Fleet), Plonker (a cabinet minister in later life), Bimbo (considered a major novelist of her generation) and the undisputed leader of our group, a towering genius, volatile, impetuous, brilliant, Timmy Waterthorpe (later to become under-manager of the bedding department of Guildford Price-rite).

Chapter 3
The Russian Revolution

I love travelling by train. I've been all o'er on my marvellous Senior Citizen's Railcard which British Rail in their generosity offer snowy-haired old codgers such as I. Makes a change from hiding in the Ladies when the ticket inspector comes round. Which, incidentally, is where I met Vladimir Ilyich Lenin on his way to the Finland Station. The Weekend Saver that Shook the World!

Hidden from History, I am. My role in the Russian Revolution has been ruthlessly suppressed. Thing is, when anyone took any pictures I always used to make sure to stand behind Trotsky because he was such a titch, poor thing, that I knew I'd be able to peep over. So when Joe Stalin had Leon scrubbed from the history books they snopaked me out and all.

Couldn't stop long. Student discounts expired in September, see.

When I came down from Cambridge, I got digs in London at first. There I soon became a key member of the Bloomsbury Group. Not, I hasten to add, that tiresome bunch of posh aesthetes and neurotics you hear so much about, but the best little poker school it's ever been my privilege to fleece.

Virginia Woolf was a neighbour of mine. I'll always remember her words to me when I popped round her house one night to scrounge a bowl of sugar: 'Betty, be it ever so humble, there's no place like home.' Not what I'd call a key contribution to modernism, but bang on for all that. Heeding her advice, I decided to return to the city of my birth, but when I arrived back to witness once again the gaslit, cobbled streets of my home town, to see those oh-so-familiar landmarks: the abattoir, the

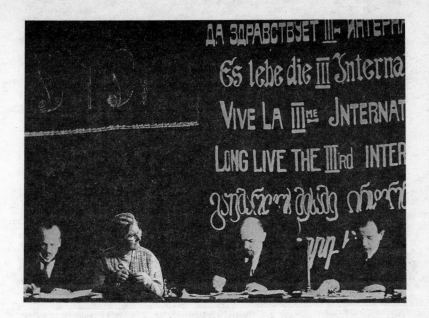

steel works, the suffragette-bedecked railings of Sheffield Town Hall, my heart grew heavy.

I threw open the door of my family's old one-up-one-down and it was as if the poor, withered little woman standing before me was a complete stranger, so raddled had she been by the ravages of hard work, childbearing and social deprivation. The ragged children who surrounded her looked on amazed as I threw myself, weeping, into her malnourished arms.

Turned out Mam had moved round the corner.

Chapter 4
Love on the Side

It was whilst working as a buffer girl – a sort of olde worlde version of a strippagram, really – that I met my first sweetheart, the father of my child and still the enduring love of my life. We never married, though. We didn't believe in that outmoded and barbaric institution.

Anyway, he was already married to my best friend. Well, actually, Arnold married Doris after him and I had started 'walking out together', as we so primly referred to it in those innocent days. Strange euphemism for copulation, that.

I felt terribly betrayed. It was my first encounter with the double standards which so bedevil the relations between male and female. Then it was quite the done thing for men to take lovers, whereas just because I earned my living giving blow-jobs to grit-shifters for ten shillings a go, I were branded a prostitute.

Not a pleasant occupation, I have to tell you. It made me feel exploited, ashamed, cut off from my community – very much how I felt later when I got a job as an audio-typist for a windscreen replacement firm in Rotherham. But times were hard and unemployment rife; I was driven to it. I'd never have done it if I'd had to *walk* to that dreary street corner.

Packed it in when I found I was pregnant. Arnold gave me the cash and I went to see the abortionist. She told me to sit in a hot bath all night, drinking gin. It's a habit I've retained ever since, though nowadays I like to add a spot of tonic and a splash of Badedas.

From then on, believe it or not of an ardent feminist such as I, but I took to pregnancy like a duck to water. The sense of deep

To Betty from Pablo. XXXX Remember?

inner harmony that comes from nurturing such a tiny, defenceless creature within one's own body is an experience which profoundly altered my entire outlook on life. When the wee darling was first put to my breast I felt at one with the cosmos, a divine earth mother, deeply enriched by my role of loving servitude at the spinning hub of the miraculous wheel of creation.

Then the little beast pissed all over me and I thought stuff this for a bunch of soldiers. It broke my young heart to do so, but I left my beloved son (no – daughter, I think it was. It were a long time ago) with my old stalwart Doris (she'd so many of her own by then I knew she'd not mind another), and set off for a much-needed break: a package trip to Sunny Spain, with that nice Mister Blair.

I sent Doris a postcard: 'For six days now we've been under constant heavy rifle- and shell-fire. Morale is low, food running out and conditions in the trenches intolerable. You'll be dead jealous of my tan, though! Love and kisses, B. xxx'

Buns and Lovers
by Arnold Bendibus
An extract

There was something strangely elderly about her, he realized suddenly and his inner spirit cowered from this dark, troubling, almost savage force which emanated from within the slim-bodied, full-skirted radiant girl-creature who stood before him, flushed from the exertions of bread-making. Her frail, bird-like fingers and splendid, naked wrists coated with the warm, uncouth dough still roused in the bearded, tousled, pale – but very interesting – young man with his curious pallor, a thick, dark, glutinous maelstrom of blind desire for her.

'Ah just popped round on't whey to't poob,' he dialected, his eyes aflame.

'Mam sezz ah'm ta stop in. Ah'm weshin mi haar.'

'Oh, aye?' He turned to go, then stopped, sullen, embarrassed, uncertain what to say. Then again he spoke.

'Tha' knowes ah'm t'be wedded, lass?' He refused to catch her eye.

'Oh, aye?'

'Aye. Dorrie Longbottom is t'be mi brahd.'

And suddenly a kaleidoscope of memories swam before their eyes, of the two of them behind that sacred bike-shed, where so often over the past few months his John Thomas and her Joan Collins had shared the beastly bliss of carnal giving, plunging again and again into the intimate depths of each other's fevered potency, swooning and shuddering.

And once they'd even had sex.

Never, never, she screamed inside, would she subjugate herself again to the fierce, desperate inner craving this sleek-buttocked young man had released in her pendulous breasts. And in her soul she was a wounded beast, howling to the moon of his phallic emanations, though on the surface her face remained still and impassive – a bit bored-looking, actually. Mind you, she thought to herself, a quick bonk on the side every once in a while might still be quite fun.

'I browarght yoo these,' he whispered, his thin, girlish voice urgent.

She looked down at his calloused yet artistic hands in which were clutched the gift he'd brought. A gift to serve as token for all the complex, quivering things he felt for her.

And Betty hated him then. Hated him in the dark, coiled bowels of her voluptuous gut, hated him, yet longed for him too in that wild, curious, unutterably queer sort of way in which women do – at least in men's novels. She shut her metaphoric inner door to him and locked it, closed the curtains, tidied up, put her feet up and wondered whether to paint the ceiling magnolia.

'You know I don't like wine gums,' she hissed.

Chapter 5
The Clouds of War and Woodbine

George Orwell came to stay with me in Sheffield once. The perfect house-guest because, unusually for a man at that time, he was terribly keen on washing up as he was doing research for a book. I had to tell him mind, 'You ought to see Wigan, mate. Things are really rough up there!'

The Great Depression had been terrible round our way too, though. The first sign of it was when the Mayor resigned, stating he was 'just too bloomin' pissed off to go on'.

The gloom spread rapidly: outbreaks of existential angst were commonplace, PMT levels shot to all-time highs, queues of ragged youths moaned on incessantly about how they just needed space to sort themselves out. Those few that could be bothered to get out of bed at all would sit listlessly on street corners reading Dostoevsky novels and humming tunes by Wagner, forerunner of the great Leonard Cohen.

We all cheered up once war was declared. Took our mind off things, somehow. Seems right callous of us now, come to think of it, but this was all in the days before 'Neighbours', remember.

The Second World War wasn't all camaraderie and Spam sandwiches, tha' knows. I was in my local on the night of the Sheffield Blitz. I just popped out the back to spend a penny when BOOM! It was indescribable. Ah, they don't make milk stout like that these days.

Recent Government legislation makes it impossible to reveal very much about my war years. A veil of secrecy must tactfully be drawn over many of my more dramatic exploits. But I am at liberty now to disclose that at one time I was dropped by parachute behind enemy lines in France to meet leaders of the Résistance who helped me set up an Old People's Home as cover for a safe house for escaped prisoners of war. These gallant lads would be smuggled in at nights when I'd disguise them as *petites vieilles femmes*.

It was this experience more than any other, I think, which alerted me to the plight of the elderly. Tragic it was to see brave men crying, pleading with me to let them try to break back into Colditz, so desperate were they to escape from a harsh regime of old-tyme dances and enforced whist drives. Plus the brutal humiliation of being teased by schoolboys and assumed to be deaf and/or stupid by Mademoiselle in the Post Office when they went to fetch their measly pensions.

Chapter 6
Post-Warrior

Pride of place at our Spitalcliffe Festival of Peace was the exhibit by Henry Moore who I'd once come across on the Northern Line during an air raid, clutching a sketchbook with a bloody great hole blown in it and muttering, 'Aye, aye!'

He sent us a most innovative bronze prototype for a throne-like commode. At least I think that's what it was. Very kind of him, I'm sure, bringing quality modern design to the people, but bloody uncomfortable.

Doris contributed 'Phablon', a towering monument to the new Welfare State built entirely of old toilet rolls, and Arnold staged a spectacular mass re-enactment of the General Strike which involved far higher police casualties than the real thing.

1956, now that were a bad year: the Suez Crisis, the Invasion of Hungary and the year they banned me from the Dog & Whistle. But that did lead me to join an Adult Ed. Writers' group to while away the long winter evenings, which led in turn to my entering the ranks of that highly influential group of writers and intellectuals known as the Angry Old Women.

I was dead excited with it all at first. Here, at last, was the voice of the outsider generation – old women barred from the private rest home elite, telling how it was in the redbrick provincial old people's flats.

Actually, most of them weren't working class at all, when I look back on it, and many weren't that old, really, either. And some of them got sickeningly cheerful after the royalty cheques came in from their first bestsellers. And then it transpired that poor Sybil wasn't even a woman, though she underwent the operation fairly soon afterwards. But we did all wear duffel coats and smoke a lot.

We were lionized by the media. John Freeman even interviewed me for his programme 'Face to Face', but he started sobbing his heart out half-way through about how he'd treated his granny, so it were never transmitted.

Gritty social realism was the order of the day and our local amateur dramatic group put on lots of the new wave of plays: *Look Forward in Fury*, *Sunday Lunchtime and Monday Elevenses*, *Flatlet at the Top* and Dorish Bendibus's stab at the new genre of everything-but-the-kitchen-sink-drama *Rose-tinted Specs*.

During the Cold War I worked as a volunteer with Meals-on-Wheels, but the political climate had turned rather chilly by then. The supervisor called me to a tribunal one morning where this official asked me, 'Are you now or have you ever been . . ?' She didn't have to say any more. I blurted out the whole story: how I had been approached by a man who claimed to be in the KGB and was paying me to send him details of irregularities in hygiene standards on microfilm embedded in stolen black puddings, so that he could discredit bourgeois welfare provision as covert euthanasia and curry favour at the Kremlin with bribes of decadent western offal produce.

I was furious with myself when it transpired they'd only wanted to know if I was allergic to sea-foods.

Rose-tinted Specs
A One Act Play
by Doris Bendibus

Scene: the Beightons' one-room flat in a large Midlands town. Well, Sheffield, actually. The audience can tell it's Sheffield because one of the characters in the play is reading the local paper.

DOLLY BEIGHTON *is reading the local paper at the table, centre stage. Dolly wears a becoming wine-red cardigan of her husband's. Somehow, beside him, her beauty appears more striking than it perhaps really is. She is a brave soul, quiet and compliant on the surface, but beneath the dowdy shell she has unexpected depths. I hope I make this apparent later on.*
ARTHUR BEIGHTON, *her husband – a bit of a one but a treasure, really, when you get to know him – stands in his shirt and underpants at the ironing-board, ironing his trousers.*
They are in the middle of a heated debate, so it's a bit hard to work out what's happening at first. But, as Stanley said at the writers' workshop, this helps to build dramatic tension.
ARTHUR *speaks first, very upset.*

ARTHUR [*very upset*]: Oh, but you wouldn't understand, would you? You don't know what it's like!
DOLLY [*helpfully*]: Sprinkle a bit of water on the creases. That'll do the trick.
ARTHUR [*bitterly*]: If only life were that simple. A quick splash of holy water and all the wrinkles washed away.

69

DOLLY [*speaking metaphorically*]: Would you like another cup of tea?

ARTHUR [*grittily realistic*]: Aye, that I would, but not too much milk this time.

[DOLLY *pours a cup of tea, just how he likes it.*]

ARTHUR [*philosophically*]: There's no place for people like me any longer. I belong in the French Revolution, or the Digger Movement, or the Spitalcliffe and District Woodcraft Folk . . . I'm out of place, out of time. Nobody knows how to live or love these days.

DOLLY [*knowingly*]: It's that blonde lass in the Crown last night calling you 'Grandad' that's bothered you, in't it, pet?

ARTHUR [*ever so angry*]: No, it bloody isn't, woman! It's far more than that, I tell you. It's this dingy flat, this bloody sick society we live in, this godawful, all-pervasive, vague sense of post-war angst!

[ARTHUR *bangs down the iron and throws his trousers dramatically across the room.*]

DOLLY [*knowingly again*]: I thought it was her. You shouldn't take it so personal.

ARTHUR [*even angrier*]: Shut your mouth, you pusillanimous cow!

DOLLY [*riled now, and who can blame her?*]: I'll not take that kind of clever talk in this house, Arthur Beighton. You've never spoken to me like that in all the twenty-three years we've been married! No, you've been a decent, good husband to me all these years on the whole. Except for that time at Violet's do but we'll not go into that.

ARTHUR [*filled with a deep sense of futility*]: 'Decent'? 'Good'? I don't know what those words mean any more! I just don't know any more!

DOLLY [*answeringly*]: That's no reason to shout!

ARTHUR [*really, really angry now!*]: But maybe the reason I'm shouting is because there's no reason! Maybe I'm sick to the backteeth with this sham of a marriage!! Maybe I've had it up to the false teeth living on the pittance the state hands out! Maybe I'm shouting because I'm slightly deaf in one ear!

DOLLY [*hearingly*]: But *I'm* not, Arthur. I'm not deaf. I hear everything, every despicable, filthy thing you say, every insult you hurl me.

[DOLLY *stands and flings her tea cup defiantly to the floor. It'll only be plastic, of course, and the tea will be cold. So even if it does splash the front row it should wipe off with a Kleenex. Then there's a pause. Very dramatic, this one.*]

DOLLY [*accusingly*]: There's another woman, isn't there? Isn't there? Spit it out! [*The truth, she means, not the tea.*]

ARTHUR [*just sort of normally*]: You know there is. You know there always has been.

71

DOLLY [*with a little laugh*]: Oh, I don't mean Betty. You know how fond I am of her, even if she can be a little – demanding sometimes. [*Well, it has to be said!*]

ARTHUR [*tender, smouldering even. If the actor can manage that*]: There's nobody else. Oh, Dolly, I'm sorry. You know how much I love you, really. It's just, it's just . . .

[DOLLY *looks at* ARTHUR *with an expression which shows how she too is no stranger to angst and vague yearnings. She knows what it is to look in the mirror and see how her looks are beginning to fade. Yet she has developed a strange sort of inner wisdom that she couldn't possibly begin to put into words but has helped her to cope with the hand fate has dealt her in the bridge game of life, and makes her glad that, for all his failings (and he's got plenty of those!), she's had* ARTHUR *as her partner through so many rubbers.*]

DOLLY: What? Just what, Arthur, my poor little squirrel?

ARTHUR: It's just that I've burnt a bloody great hole in my best pair of trousers.

THE END

Chapter 7
Granny Takes a Trip

Most people say they can remember exactly what they were doing on the night that President Kennedy was assassinated. Strange as it may seem for one such as I, with a photographic memory going back so far that my early recollections are not so much sepia-tinted as etched engravings, I can't.

However, I can vividly recall what young Stan Glossop were doing to me and very pleasant it was too until the newsflash came on and he lost all control.

I'd been in regular correspondence with the great man (Kennedy, that is, not Glossop, who was nice enough in his way but hardly of towering status even in the world of South Yorkshire Chiropody) since the day he flew over to support us in our campaign against the close-down of Sheffield's only night-spot for transvestites, the infamous Bierkeller Klub. It was at the portals of that notorious watering-hole that Johnny came out for the first time in public with his bold declaration: '*Ich bin ein Belinda!*'

It was Martin Luther King's demise which was the real blow to me. He'd been such a sweety when I was over in the States for the Civil Rights Tour. We were on our way to a gig in Alabama (a great double act, us; he'd warm up the crowd with a lecture on racialism and then I'd show them how to cook perfect Yorkshire Pudding), and we both fell asleep on the Greyhound bus. He woke up, yawned, stretched and then looked at me most strangely. 'Betty,' he said, 'I just had the most extraordinary dream.'

'Martie, what a coincidence!' I said. 'So did I!' And I told him all about it. Mine involved being stuck in a lift with Dolly Fargate, Adam Faith and Mandy Rice-Davies. I can't recall what his was about.

'We had a dream . . .'

But I feel I rather missed out on the swinging sixties (they were more sort of dangling, really, up here in Sheffield) era of mop-topped popsters, jolly bobbies, Labour majorities, political satirists and men from uncle.

I lived a very settled existence working as a courier for a local travel agency. Had some nice working holidays, though. Like Haight-Ashbury in '67. I'd picked up this awful tummy bug, but kind Doctor Leary gave me some wonderful pills for it.

Paris in the spring of '68. I've got a lovely snap of me and Simone de Beauvoir outside the Sorbonne. Lovely lady. It was her husband I couldn't stand. 'Existentialist' they called him. 'Pain-in-the-arsist', if you ask me.

And it was whilst on a package tour to India that year that a guru I met at the Kathmandu Bureau de Change explained to me how the divine light was only visible to those over sixty and wearing bifocals. It was Sri Elsie's inspiration which led me to throw off the trivial shell of middle-aged selfhood and enter a permanent state of cosmic retirement from shallow materialism.

But my home life was terribly dull till the day I took a busload of shoppers down to London for the sales and we broke down right outside the American Embassy in Grosvenor Square. At the height of the rioting, a rather tasty old man in a kaftan slipped a leaflet into my hand before he was clubbed to the ground by the mounted police. It read:

WE ARE OLD AND WE ARE ANGRY

There is a new/old spirit sweeping Albion, freaking out the brain-dead straights of middle-aged middlingdom.

We are a tribe of psychedelic elderfolk: white revolutionaries, witches, wizards and Wincarnis-heads living together in cosmic togetherness in 'Galadriel', a communal rest-home just a short magic bus ride from the World's End.

Join us! Share your money, body, sandwiches, bifocals with everyone!

Act *now*. Go to a supermarket, load up a trolley full of boil-in-the-bag brown rice paella meals for one, stand at the check-out and refuse to pay till they legalize marijuana and euthanasia.

Squat. It's far more comfortable than standing.

Come together. Assemble in Hyde Park next Sunday for a day of drugs, fucks and duck-feeding.

WE ARE THE PEOPLE YOUR PARENTS
WARNED YOU NOT TO ACCEPT SWEETS FROM

WE ARE THE GRUMPY BRIGADE

Ah, those heady days of free love and free dental check-ups.

Of course, my old friend Karl Marx was a proto-hippy, really. I was always saying to him – 'Karl,' I used to say, 'your concept of surplus value may be looking a bit outmoded in a few years' time, but I reckon that hair-do of yours could have lasting significance.'

Exit 33
by Arnold Bendibus, Snr

Introduction by Sir Stanley Netheredge, Q.C.

Of all the famous obscenity trials of the late fifties and early 1960s none perhaps attracted the scandalized attention of the general public and the outspoken support of certain notorious figures within the literary establishment less than that of *The Crown* v. *Whiplash Press*, publishers of *Exit 33* by Arnold Bendibus.

Even so, during the ten-minute-long trial, a string of key witnesses testified movingly to the book's brilliance, its allegorical nature and deeply moral purpose. That the judge disallowed their evidence on the grounds that experience in car mechanics and hairdressing did not qualify them to act as experts in the field of modern literature remains a shocking indictment of a society which believed that great works of fiction could only be appreciated by those who could read.

At the time, *Exit 33* was naively dismissed as nothing but a smutty book about Arnold, Betty, and his wife. Recently it has been reappraised as a text in which the narrator, A. (both a self-portrait of the artist and the first letter of the alphabet), his lover (who exists as a discrete fictional entity and perhaps more significantly as a cluster of three typed figures which we take when congregated next to one another to signify the name 'Bet' upon the page), and the linguistic construct labelled 'Dorrie', his wife, are held together in a narrative structure liable to create genital arousal in the reader as decoder.

Thus, with hindsight, it seems extraordinary that people could ever have been so small-minded as to deem pornographic the

graphic description of the gratuitous sexual exploits of a foul-
mouthed old pervert couched in language of no literary merit
whatsoever.

EXIT 33

An extract

Eeeeeeeeeeeeeeeeeeeeeeeeeeeeeeeeeeeeeeeeeeeeeeeeeee
eeeeeeeeeeeeeeeeeeeeeee !!! by gum but I'm plastered brain
reeling eyes popping gut wobbling stumbling out of the gaumont
bet pushing me into the doorway of thicketts the pork butcher
for a quickie god she's hot always like this after a good norman
wisdom picture hand down mi demob suit trousers she growls
in her throat gimme gimme but can't lay her hands on the half
bottle of bells i got stuffed down mi pants dingaling dingalong
feel her wringing the juice from me I stumble and kick over a bin
full of old chip papers crying hey whatchit bet almost suffered a
rupture pack it in or we'll go missin our bus
    arm in arm down to the bus station sheffield on a hot barmy
night the sweet scents of diesel vomit and vinegar mingling bringing up that lump in the back of the throat that meanseeeeeeee
eeeeeeeeeeeeeeeeeee to be back on the open road hitching
maybe just outside newark feeling the wind in mi hair and bits
of cold cheeseburger between mi teeth from the four seasons grill
at the services met a chick there once called maria i ogled till she
said hiya blue eyes you fancy it do you and when i said you bet
squirted a tomato-shaped pot of heinz ketchup up in the air like
a long jet of sperm in an arc weeeeeeeeee landing smack on
mi baldpatch
    dorrie said once i resembled the buddha me in mi y fronts or
some big fat slob poor doris back ome mi poor little wifey all
lonesome alone with nowt but a crate of peculiar and an ounce
of red leb she'll be high as a kite when we get back for cocoa
hope she dont spike it with acid like last night when i thought in
mi dreams i can fly and woke up with mi head in the pisspot

torn between two chicks me not spring ones exactly but tender for all that both nuts about me god o god how i suffer from guilt for this surfeit of love mind you then again lately things have been a bit sort of w e e e e e e e e e eird since dorrie said whynot-bringherroundthenyerbitonthewatchercallitside they hit it off great all giggling and whispers then dorrie sez be a pet love and pop down t'pub or summat willya and gerrus a babycham when i got back there were no sign of life just this groaning and breath-ing sound coming from bedroom i were gobsmacked thought weyhey an orgy burst in wi mi trousers down round mi ankles then dorries voice from the darkness says be a pet love and pop down the chippy mines cod and bet wants mushy peas we all three share a bed now and i'm on the outside and somehow its muggins here as allus fetches tea in the mornin while they have some nooky o o o e e e e e e e e e e e e e e e e e how i suffer

oh but bet and i now at the back of the bus she finding and downing mi bells in one swig mutters hungry lascivious gurglings sliding her lips down mi chest slips down on her knees puts her face in mi lap not here we'll be seen oh but wow what the hell us two bums on the road of the wild generation us devil may care types in the fast lane anyroad bus lane of life and stuff suck me oh baby oh do it oh do it i pant beg and howl and a bus full of ladies on t'way back from bingo start laughing their heads off as bet starts to snore

Chapter 8
Oldwomenonly

It were all a load of male-dominated media lies designed to degrade us, that myth about we early pensioner 'libbers' burning our corsets as a publicity stunt at the first National Elderly Women's Conference. The damn things wouldn't catch light, so then I tore the trousers off this photographer bloke from the *Guardian* and they went up much better.

At first there was just the one autonomous elderwomen's group in SPLAF. Then a second group was formed for working-class women only, then the women of colour and colour-blindness set up groups of their own, then there were special groups for the radical lesbians and the socialist spinsters. So I formed a working-class, radical-socialist bisexual grannies' group, which I must say raised my consciousness to previously undreamt of heights. Though after a year or two I got a bit fed up with my own company and packed it in.

Our peace camp was wonderful. We surrounded the site, festooned the wire with pictures and ribbons and hand-crocheted tea-cosies, linked arms and sang songs like 'Spinsterhood is Powerful', 'Great Aunts Together are Strong' and 'We Do Like to be Beside the Seaside'. But those sexist redcoats still wouldn't let us in half-price.

I met Gavin during that period. He was very big in Young Men's Groups, which have their detractors, I know, but do have their role. Gavin's organized the toilet arrangements at our conferences, produced a newsletter called 'Unbecoming Young' and run seminars on 'Celebrating Hair Loss'. I think it's terribly important for young men to take responsibility for their own ageism and seek to eliminate it. Though why that involves groups of them meeting round at each other's houses to talk about masturbation for hours on end I never could fathom.

It was a tremendous boost to the confidence, of course, for an immature young whelp like him to have a gorgeous mature woman fall hopelessly in love with him. At last he'd met someone with the experience to see through his peachy, beefcake exterior to the gnarled being within. There were them as cracked jokes about my 'Gerontoyboy', but I'll not mention names – not even Alice Fargate's. We cared naught for the scandalmongers.

We first met at a benefit shindig for WAA (Waltz Against Ageism) and of course I was rather shy because I knew I'd have to make the first move with the kind of chap who wears badges saying WOLF-WHISTLING IS RAPE. In the event it was all very natural. We got chatting, we danced together – his quickstep was divine. Later he offered me a lift home in his 2CV. I invited him in for a Nicaraguan Carob juice and the inevitable happened: we became celibates.

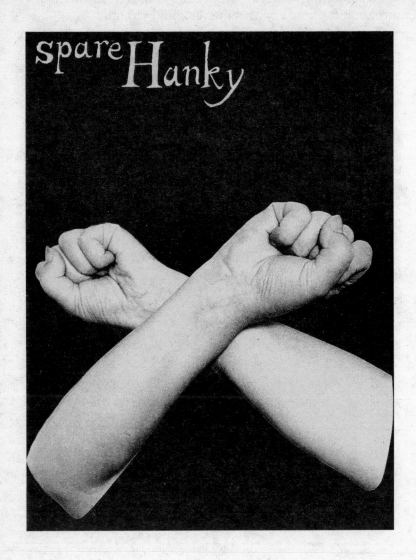

Chapter 9
The Enemy Within

In the mid eighties I had a little business going as a Holistic Menopause Consultant on Enterprise Allowance. I managed to get in to see Margaret Thatcher that way, pretending I was touting for trade. It was tough getting through the security at Number 10, but it's amazing how doors open for you when you're brandishing a speculum.

To my astonishment, I found Mrs T. to be a most pleasant lady. Don't know how she survives the harsh cut and thrust of politics, though. She was up in her bedroom sobbing her eyes out. I didn't introduce myself, but at that moment she was so much in need of support from a fellow radical pensioner that she just fell into my arms and blurted out the whole story.

She'd just been rowing with her husband because he wanted the Miners crushed and she'd said she couldn't do such a rotten thing to such a fine body of hard-working, perhaps wrong-headed but essentially decent, men. But Denis had gone into one of his moods and she'd just had to give in to him.

Apparently it's only to please her Denis that she pretends to be so vicious. Left to herself she'd rather be darning his socks and knocking up soufflés in that dream home in Dulwich. But, apparently, like so many men of his age, he's terribly sexually insecure and can only get it up if she acts all dominant. I know you wouldn't think he'd be interested in sex at all to look at him, but she herself has admitted publicly that she only gets five hours' sleep a night.

A classic example of the oppressive power of male sexual fantasy. Starts with a bit of mistress/slave role-play in the privacy of the bedroom, ends up with the Poll Tax and impersonating the

Queen to visiting dignitaries in a desperate attempt to stimulate his jaded appetites.

She was terribly ashamed when she came to her senses and realized what she'd blurted out to me, a complete stranger. I suppose I could have blackmailed her, but when all's said and done, I thought, she too is a sister. And she had such a winning little smile. So I sold her a copy of my pamphlet 'Decoding Sexist Language' and left it at that.

I know some of my male comrades might think I did wrong. But if I'd lost my temper with her she'd only have got all stroppy and defensive. Well, you know how she is: her Argentinian cleaning lady tells her off for getting mud on the parquet and the next day it's war in the Falklands.

And it has given me pleasure over the years to watch her sacking male ministers one after the other. Because it said in my book that when a man says to a woman 'With all due respect, Ma'am, it must be said I slightly disagree with — ' what he really means is 'Stop yattering and get your knickers down, you bird-brained piece of fluff.'

CM: Betty, I gather that your pensioners' group publishes a little newsletter . . .

Betty: *Right! That's it! Get out! I'll not be patronized any longer by this bumptious little pimply!*

CM: But . . .

Betty: *'Little newsletter'?! I'll have you know 'Age War' is at the forefront when it comes to the latest media technology, since we appropriated Agenda's word processor.*

CM: I didn't mean . . .

Betty: *And we have full-colour photography, thanks to Doris and her watercolours!*

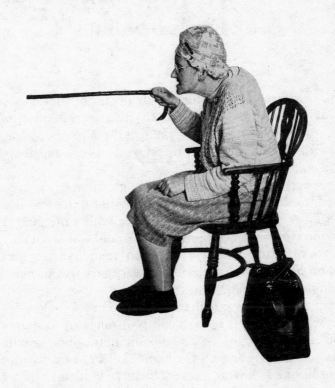

CM: It's obviously a much larger operation than I'd been led to believe . . .

Betty: *Our news gathering service is on a par with Fleet Street, I'll have you know!*

CM: Oh, really?

Betty: *Oh, aye. When I want a scandalous story of official corruption I just call my investigative journalist Eric Fargate at his fortress-style premises on the flats and he makes one up.*

CM: Look, I'm terribly sorry if I've upset you . . .

Betty: *Just watch it, that's all, sunbeam!*

The Making of 'Age War'
by Doris Bendibus

We've been bringing out our weekly organ for some years now and my how it's grown! When Betty first suggested we publish some kind of newsletter we all thought this a terrific idea and set to immediately. Little did we realize then how much work it would entail!

In the early days it was a simple enough affair. Betty, of course, was editor and wrote all the articles. After much cajoling and flattering remarks about my technique with Cow gum, I was persuaded to do the laying-out. And Arnold was given the arduous task of distribution. He was soon a familiar figure around town on his trusty Hercules three-gear, packages of newsprint stuffed in his panniers!

From the outset we realized that the 'visual look' of it was extremely important. I 'mocked up' a range of 'concepts' for 'mastheads' and 'logos' (got a book out of the library on this, so I knew all the jargon). Of the many sketches I executed, Betty chose this one as having a classic blend of boldness and accessibility:

AGE WAR

Early issues contained a, I hope, diverting blend of home hints, reminiscences and some really rather indigestible chunks of polemic from lesser known Bolsheviks of Betty's acquaintance. I did the gardening tips and Arnold gave us some of his lovely poems to put in, which was kind.

It was only a couple of mimeographed sheets of foolscap stapled together of course, and sales were to say the least slack till Arnold's poem comparing my genitalia to an orchid in bloom and the then MP for Spitalcliffe East to Judas Iscariot brought us some notoriety, a stiff fine and a huge growth in readers.

Our original logo was looking just a wee bit staid by the late swinging sixties and although I must say an old stick such as I felt just a little out of her depth trying to dream up something 'groovy' enough for that fashion-conscious decade, one night I dropped a few tabs of LSD to aid inspiration and came up with this:

The next change of face came early in the 1980s but it's already tending to look a bit dated now, I fear.

AGE WAR

Recently we've had yet another face-lift and, I know some of you may not approve of this, but we now have a Page Three. It seemed a waste of paper to leave it blank. In the first issue there's a topless photo of myself and Arnold in passionate embrace under the headline AVOID HYPOTHERMIA – SLEEP WITH A FRIEND. It's rather tasteful, we think, though the photo being topless, you can't see our faces which seems a shame. Underneath it says KEEP CANOODLING BUT CARRY A CONDOM SPITAL WARNS RANDY GRANNIES. So you can't accuse us of irresponsible journalistic practices.

Its sports page, unparalleled in its coverage of bowls (carpet and outdoor), whist, Scrabble and sumo wrestling competitions, has won it readers from all walks of life. Always keen to improve our service to disadvantaged groups in society, we recently followed the lead of *Sunday Sport* by appointing a full-time Spiritualist Correspondent to cover stories concerning our comrades in the dead community.

Ayj Woar

It *whirr*
joos tuthah deh
Ah wur standin bytsiyed of troad
toutin Ayjwoar
wen coppa coomoop he sez:
Eee, Ah'm afeard
Thar carnt flog thi pehper
rowndere pal, he sez,
he sez, carnt flog thi pehper
rowndere.

Nah then: choofoff cok aye sez to im,
doernt coom thacrap wi mee sunbeem
ee sez choofoff thissen balldi!
Oudi thinkyizz godallcchuffinmyti?
I sed tooim, jusyooweyut pal
till revlooshun cooms
yerl bi ferst ti bi
oop ergenst worl
thenny grabdmi rount throwart
sez: aye – 'n jusyooweyut 'n orl!

nah ah bin don fa pozeshun
ovanoffensive weppon – loyah rekkons ayl koppit.
Eeeeeeeeeeeeeeeeeeeeeeeeeeeeeeeeeeeeeeeeeeeeeeee!
Wots werld coominto wen theh corlit a crym
t'havva sheffeeyld steell bleyd inyer pokkit?

*

wekkup ye twerliz vrom yer snoozin
fetchyer warkinstix ov gowld
fetchyer zimmerfrayms ov fiyar –
wi shalnot seese frem growin owld

91

anthi wayjes o'sin mebbe deth
bot thi wayjes wigget arra bloominsyt werse —
so joynin thi penshuners songkomrids —
ark tethe werds o' mi verss!

izzit a crym t'tell trooerth as ya seeit?
izzit a crym t'stundoop fer thissen?
boogertha yung uns! komrids aryz!
Lesgo wayjin ayj woar agen!
boogertha yung uns! komrids aryz!
Lesgo wayjin ayj woar agen!

ARNOLD BENDIBUS[1]

1. For the last decade Arnold Bendibus has refused to write in any language but his own mother tongue. Acknowledging the influence of poets such as Benjamin Zephaniah and Stanley Holloway, Bendibus believes Yorkshire dialect to be the only adequate vehicle with which to explore the unique cultural context of the Sheffield Pensioner, rich as it is with a vocabulary that has no direct equivalent in Standard English. For instance, seventeen different adjectives describing different textures of parkin, a popular local delicacy.

It was in the 'Ode to My Sweetheart on Returning from the Gaumont' that he first made his bold linguistic pledge: 'Shizz a birrov olrite izz owr bet pet/fer er ot battered bodi aye ache/shigor ayes as delishuss as green mooshi peez/ aye, an flesh thatsus soft assa breadcaik. /Ahm inspyrd ta ryte evvry tahm tharaye kisser/ ah — boot norrin tha langwidge o' mi soothen orpresser.'

His next dialect piece, 'Christ Comes to Bramall Lane' was considered outrageous when first published in 'Age War'. But what is so outrageous after all about the Messiah — who certainly never spoke the English of King James — voicing his opinions in broad Yorkshire (or for that matter being depicted attending a football match after a night out clubbing with a homosexual truck driver from Inverness)?

Bendibus sets himself firmly in the oral tradition and performs his poetry live in local clubs with the aid of a backing tape of scratch Max Jaffa remixes.

[Ed.]

Self-Defence for the Elderly
The Pensioner Mugs Back

Despite media claims to the contrary, the statistics suggest that it is young men, not women or the elderly, who are the most likely victims of unprovoked violent attack on the streets, which is fair enough, really, as for one reason or another young men are bound to deserve it, whereas innocent pensioners have enough on their plates already without having to contend with vicious little muggers all the while.

More insidious by far, however, is the psychological harassment we old folk have come to identify as 'mind-mugging', an as yet unrecognized crime for which we would like to see the implementation of stiff prison sentences and public birchings if we believed in that sort of thing – which, of course, we don't.

But SPLAF has already started to lobby parliament to introduce a Bill aimed at tackling pensioner abuse by giving social workers far-reaching powers to place adults under custody orders and subject them to unspeakably humiliating medical examinations if there is the faintest suspicion that they may not be treating elderly parents with the respect and veneration they deserve.

Social workers claim to be caught in a cleft stick, criticized on the one hand for intervening and on the other for failing to intervene in family disputes. We would like to see all pre-retired members of society placed in exactly the same cleft stick. Whilst this might result in thousands of innocent people suffering needlessly, it's surely a small price to pay if the result is one member of the elder community resting more easily in his or her bed (or anyone else's for that matter).

For the time being, however, pensioners must fend for themselves against mental and physical cruelty, and the following tips may prove useful.

WARNING: SOME OF THESE TECHNIQUES CAN PROVE DANGEROUS IF USED BY THOSE WITH SERIOUS HEART CONDITIONS OR CRIMINAL RECORDS

We use as the basis for our techniques the ancient martial art of Fuey Tu Yung, practised by Zen masters on cheeky young students since time immemorial.

Some basic 'Fuey' moves include:

- The Sound of One Hand Clapping: In which the Zen master belts his assailant round the ear.
- The Fourfold Path: In which he kicks him in the knees, groin, chest and head, then walks right over him.
- The Bringer of Enlightenment: Knocking your assailant unconscious with a blunt instrument can also have the beneficial outcome of helping him to attain Nirvana, a blissful state of cosmic non-being.

As you can see, Fuey Tu Yung is essentially non-violent. At its heart is the eastern philosophy that water can overcome stone and the weak can win over the strong. In the words of Lao Tsu:

> One who excels in travelling leaves no wheel tracks;
> One who excels in borrowing leaves no fingerprints;
> Therefore the sage hits out
> And retires to Hastings;
> That is the way of heaven.

There are many potentially violent situations which can be nipped in the bud if avoidance tactics are taken early.

SITUATION: You see the man from Radio Rentals drive up in his van to repossess your telly.
TACTIC: Switch off all lights and hope he gives up and goes away, thinking you must have popped round to the neighbours. If instead, he assumes you're lying unconscious on the floor after a fall and starts breaking the door down, shout

through the letter-box that you've only this minute woken up, that he's welcome to come in but you are still highly infectious.

Sometimes, however, there is no alternative to the use of force.

SITUATION: Your local library has still not got hold of a copy of the new Catherine Cookson which you first ordered weeks ago. The librarian keeps waffling on about understaffing and computer breakdowns but you suspect sheer inefficiency.

TACTIC: A swift rabbit punch to the stomach should ensure speedy delivery.

The classic Fuey Tu Yung approach is to mix aggression with passivity, disarming the potential aggressor thus:

SITUATION: A policeman is barring your way to the senior government minister you wish to speak to in person.
TACTIC: An elbow to the stomach and a knee in the groin, then, when he pulls out his truncheon, feign a heart attack. When he runs to get medical assistance, nip in through the door.

EGO: Puncture it with a merciless quip.

EARS: A good loud tirade of verbal abuse can work wonders.

EYES: Show him you mean business by fixing him with a steely glint. If that fails, ask him to come a little closer as you're a jot hard of hearing, then jab with two fingers.

CLOTHING: Knitting him a really horrible jumper and regularly making sure he still feels he ought to wear it can grind down the confidence of a troublesome relation.

INSTITUTIONAL POWER: Always harder to deal with. Letters to the media, hunger marches and armed insurrection are all possibilities but take time. Engineering a sex scandal can eradicate unwanted individuals, but governments are harder to shift. General strikes are one answer, but for more fool-proof personal relief leaving the country may, at the present moment, be the only answer.

SEXUAL HARASSMENT: Groping and kissing an assailant can disarm him temporarily.

BOTTOM: A well-aimed slap with your stick may rekindle childhood terrors of elders in authority. Be warned that it may turn him on, mind.

FEET: It is possible to do severe damage to these without the potential assailant even realizing you're on the attack. Stamp your boot down hard, say, 'Oh, I'm terribly sorry. I didn't see you there, dearie' and he'll probably apologize to you.

STICK

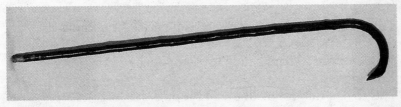

Unscrew the handle to reveal small flask for Dutch courage. Press secret knob to activate bayonet mechanism.

Try holding your walking-stick aloft and shouting: 'By the Power of Greyskull!' to frighten assailants before you crack 'em one on the bonce.

THE HANDBAG

Spray paint disguised as hairspray
Brick
Jiffy lemon
Photos of naked babies (all-purpose)
A little light reading
Condom (useful as a waterbomb on demos, if nothing else)
Stickers: THIS PERSON HATES LITTLE OLD LADIES
False bottom to bag, handy for 'shopping'
Knitting
Plastic bag full of bits of bread for duck-feeding
Lipstick (also useful for graffiti)
Portable cellphone to contact the world media, if arrested

Property Page
by Agenda Overleaf

Isn't it awful how everyone goes on and on about house prices these days. Nicko and I just hate it.

Whenever we have friends up from London they're no sooner through the door than cooing over what a des. res. we've got and how lucky we were to get it before the boom and how prices are ridiculous down South now and they're so desperate they've been reduced to living in cardboard boxes under the arches at Waterloo. Positively yawn-making.

Sometimes we do get a bit rattled and feel we have to point out what a risk we took when we bought this place because at that time it was simply horrid round here and nobody at all lived in this part of town. At least nobody us-ish, if you know what I mean.

Actually we've already had a look at the nursery near here with Sproglet in mind and it's brilliant. Very multinational. They celebrate Eid and Chinese New Year and Stevie Wonder's birthday . . . And at Christmas they sing special carols that no one knows the words of, just to make sure we all feel in the same boat.

Getting to know Asian people has been fantastic. You get a wonderful broad cultural perspective on life buying disposable nappies from Mr Mohammed.

And Jereboam Ezekiel Rastaman (Bill to his friends) has invited us to go to one of those blues clubs with him. I don't know what I think about porno-things these days, but it's a different culture of course and I keep telling Nicko he ought to go just out of politeness and it would be so interesting seeing.

But honestly I think this obsession with money is a real sign of the ghastly times we live in, don't you? Anyway, no doubt that's a bit irrelevant for you, I expect, as you're probably living in somewhere rented or in a home or geriatric ward, or else some quaint little terrace, which you bought for about 1/6d ninety-odd years ago and is probably worth a small fortune these days, you lucky devils, though of course it'll be filled with sentimental memories which makes it quite different. But you never know, you just might consider selling some time, mightn't you. So I thought it might be useful if I just filled you in a bit on 'The Property Scene' in case it should ever come in useful.

HOUSES

Basically, houses are out. Far too expensive for people like you and not practical, anyway. You'd get so lonely rattling about in an old pile like we live in, I assure you.

INSTITUTIONS

A lot of old mental homes are coming on to the market now, so it might be worth a group of you clubbing together and buying one. You could all live together like a sort of commune and turn the old ECT-treatment room into a Bingo hall or whatever you fancy. Just a thought, but grim as Rampton might appear from the outside, I'll bet it's simply crammed full of the most marvellous cornices and built-in cupboards and those little touches which can up the price no end once you've bought it for a song and bunged in a few ruched curtains. And then there's hospitals, of course, and libraries soon quite probably. Criminal as it is, the demolition of the welfare state does provide exciting opportunities for the first-time buyer.

(I do keep worrying whether all this sounds terribly middle class to you. I suppose it probably does but then I am, aren't I? Though, to be honest, Dad wasn't exactly a *top-ranking* civil servant. But I gather guilt is a bit old hat now, so I try not to worry. It's amazing how political it's made me already though, living up here. I get simply livid watching 'Question Time' these days. Betty would have been proud of me if she'd heard what I shouted at Sir Robin Day just last week. Nicko, bless him, was terribly shocked.)

GRANNYFLATS

When Nicko and I went to New York last year (swank, swank – sorry!), we stayed in one of those lofts and that set us thinking. Don't you think these old coal cellars you all have round here would make just dinky grannyflats? Have to take the coal out first, of course! But, joking apart, they could be made into utterly scrummy little garden flats – if you've got a garden.

Now, the Big Question facing pensioners on a small income, living alone is: post-modernist or neo-country when considering interior decor. Obviously a matter of personal taste, but do bear in mind what a doddle it is to clean those bare white walls and plain floorboards which are so much the rage. Whereas cluttering the place up with dusty knick-knacks and flea-bitten carpets is tantamount to asking for chronic asthma and water on the knee.

Then again, if you like where you are, then stay is my advice. Honestly, we begged Nicko's mum on bended knee to move up and live with us. She stubbornly refused once we'd pointed out what a tip it'll be once the baby's born and how miserable she'd be away from her friends and she'd have no Mrs Evans to pop in and do for her, that's for sure.

So proud, aren't you, you lot. I respect that so much.

'My Favourite Things'
Pastimes for the Autumn Years

Sadly it tends to be only managing directors, long-term prisoners and the like with plenty of spare time on their hands who get the chance to indulge in those leisure pursuits so vital in keeping the mature mind relaxed, fit and healthy.

But elderly people too need to take an occasional break from the hectic rat race of retirement and make time for pastimes and hobbies.

Here are some of the recreational diversions I personally find most rewarding:

A great pleasure for me in my old age has been my garden. There's nothing quite like that wonderful sense of fulfilment and oneness with nature that I get when I look out of my back window to see that army of young offenders on community service orders working their lovely little bottoms off, applying horse droppings to my cannabis plants.

I have a small vegetable patch. My taste buds may have bloomed and withered years back, but I still get great pleasure from preparing and eating food. I'm a confirmed vegetarian myself; after all some of my best friends are married to vegetables.

MEAT IS MURDER the slogan goes and it's absolutely true; my friend Sybil was horribly killed a few months back by a salmonella-infested, shrink-wrapped, pre-cooked roast chicken intent on revenge. But I do make an exception for fish. As poor Edwina Curry so rightly pointed out, we Northerners consume little else but beer and fish and chips – though of course for years now we've cooked them *à la nouvelle cuisine*.

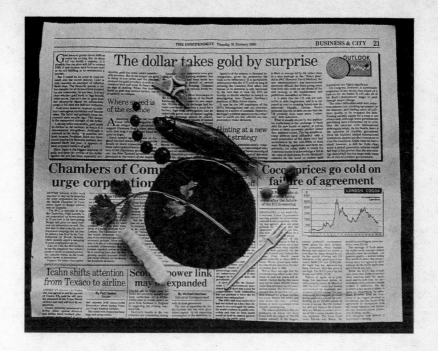

Consumer Fetishism and the Designer Pensioner

Shopping for cheap clothes in the sales is something many pensioners enjoy, but I do find it a bit of a bore. All those hours spent in packed, stuffy shops with disgruntled assistants running about fetching me different items to try on can be tedious in the extreme. But it's worth it all for the joy of taking my purchases back the next day and demanding a cash refund because they clash with the dining-room wallpaper.

The Opiates of the People and Where to Procure Them

A well-stocked medicine cupboard is essential for those whose health may be gradually failing, and can provide hours of fun. Mine contains items purchased from any good chemist, Leroy on the flats, the Nuthouse and Aggie Glossop's Quaint Olde Remedies and Home Distillery Suppliers.

Health and Efficiency

I've become a bit of a fitness freak lately. Joined the local athletic club when I found out it was cutprice for the Over 60s. I don't take part in competitions, of course; I don't believe in that sort of thing. I just go for the companionship and the steroids.

Each morning before setting off on her hectic schedule of campaigning, Betty sets time aside to prepare for the pressures ahead by listening to a tape, specially recorded by Gavin Youngperson, SPLAF's resident therapist, which you too may find useful:

[Ed.]

Sit in a comfortable chair with the curtains drawn and the phone off the hook, close your eyes and follow my instructions:

Lean back in your seat, breathe deeply, close your eyes, relax. Really relax now.

I want you to concentrate on any tensions in your body. In your back, your neck, your guts, your shoulders. Really feel those tensions. Concentrate those tensions into your shoulders. Now, hunch them up tight. Tight as tight. Now, hold on to that tension.

But let your mind float free . . . Think back over the past twenty-four hours to any little incidents that left you feeling irritated, niggled, uptight, fraught. Remember your way back into those feelings. Try to recapture in your mind the way you felt then.

Now focus on your body. Imagine your arms going heavy, so heavy you can't even move them. Then picture in your mind that you're itchy all over, covered in horrible, tiny little mites. You want to scratch them, don't you? You're just dying to scratch but, remember, you can't move your arms.

Lie still and concentrate on holding on to these feelings of annoyance, frustration. Let them build to a peak of sheer bloody fury . . .

Then open your eyes, stand up, put your coat on and . . .

GO OUT THERE AND GIVE 'EM HELL!

Style wars – A Radical Chic Intervention

Off-duty, Betty likes to relax in jeans and a tee-shirt, saucy short skirts or sophisticated evening-wear, but when campaigning out on the streets, the classic look of the archetypal Twerly is a must.

Get knitted this winter with sumptuous swathes of figure-hugging pure wool. Cardigan necklines plunge to reveal static-crackling man-made fibres. Figure-hugging skirts reflect a nostalgic mood, and worn over clinging support stockings in this year's sultriest shade of elastoplast pink give that 'look don't touch' message to menacing muggers.

Make up: Eye-brows are worn high this year. Smudged lipstick is *de rigueur.*
Hat: Jaunty headdress (£58.95) from Edwina of Knightsbridge.
Accessories: Add that special *je ne sais quoi exactement* to even the plainest outfits.

Fashion Predictions for 1990:
Sexy teddies are out. Liberty bodices are back with a bang. Janet Reger unveils her first thermal collection. Jasper Conran gets into galoshes.

'CHIC AHOY!'

Stitches Plain and Buttons Pearly, The Cardie Knit for Every Twerly

(Designed by Paula Hurst for the United Colourist Republic of Betty)

Materials

6 50g balls double-knitting main colour
1 50g ball double knitting black
3 pearly buttons
1 pr 3¼mm needles
1 pr 4mm needles
To fit size 38–40in bust

Front

With size 3¼mm needles cast on 103 sts.
Work K1, P1 rib for 8cm.
Change to 4mm needles.
Work 8 rows st st and at each end of 9th and
    every foll 8th row inc. 1 st.
Work until 117 sts on needle.
Work straight until front measures 33cm
    ending with P row.

Shape Armholes

Cast off 6 st at beg. of next 2 rows.
Dec. 1 st at each end of next 5 rows.
Dec. 1 st at each end of next 3 alt rows (89
    sts).
Work straight until armhole measures 16cm
    ending with P row.

Shape Neck

Work 38 sts, cast off 13 sts, work to end.
Cont. on last set of stitches
Dec. 1 st at neck edge on next 6 rows and

then the 4 alt. rows, ending at armhole
    edge.

Shape Shoulder

Dec. at neck edge on alt. rows twice more.
At same time cast off 7 sts at beg. of next
    row and 6 sts at beg. of 2 foll. alt. rows.
Work 1 row. Cast off.
Rejoin yarn to rem. sts at neck edge and
    complete to match 1st side, working 1
    more row before shoulder-shaping.

Back

Foll. patt. as for front up to shoulder-shaping,
    reading from chart when work measures
    27cm. When chart finishes, work straight
    until shoulder-shaping, right-side facing.

Shape Shoulders and Back of Neck

Cast off 7 sts at beg. of next 2 rows.
Next row cast off 6 sts, K16 sts (including st
    on needle), cast off 31 sts, K to end.
Cont. on last set of stitches
1st row cast off 6 sts, P to last 2 sts, P2 tog.
2nd row K2 tog., K to end.
3rd row as 1st.
Work 1 row and then cast off rem. 7 sts.
Rejoin yarn
1st row P2 tog., P to end.
2nd row cast off 6 sts, K to last 2 sts, K2 tog.
3rd row as 1st and then cast off rem. 7 sts.

Sleeves

With 3¼mm needles cast on 71sts.
Work K1, P1 rib for 8 rows.
Change to 4mm needles.
Inc. 1 st at each end of next row and then
    every foll. 6th row until 81 sts on needle.
Work until sleeve measures 15cm ending
    with P row.

Shape Top

Cast off 6 sts at beg. of next 2 rows.
Now dec. 1 st at each end of every row until
    55 sts rem., then every alt. row until 33 sts
    rem., then every row until 19 sts rem.
Cast off.

Make up and Neck Border

Join right shoulder seam. With 3¼mm
    needles and right side facing pick up and
    knit 21 sts down left side of front neck-
    edge 13 sts from cast off st, 21 sts up right
    side of neck and 44 sts evenly along back
    neck-edge.
Work K1, P1 rib for 8 rows and cast off.
Join left shoulder and neck border seam.
Join side and sleeve seams.
Sew sleeves into armholes.
Sew 3 buttons down centre front 2.5cm apart.

Strut funky stuff.

Dear Maudie

A favourite feature of 'Age War' since its inception has been the 'Dear Maudie' page, containing news of SPLAF members past and present, plus Margery Hackenthorpe's unique blend of tips, quotes and advice on everything from removing stains on carpets to shifting cabinet ministers from high-ranking office.

[Ed.]

Hello, Splaffers! Here I am again! Doesn't time fly?!

It seems only last week that I was writing my last letter to you all. As indeed it was.

By the way, as the evenings draw in and winter approaches, don't forget your flu jabs, will you?!

@@@@@@@@

Doris Bendibus popped round on Friday with the deeply distressing news that Brenda (Wicker née Darnall) is sadly no longer with us. I'm sure you'll all remember her well from the Hunger Strike days. Apparently she's moved to Margate to be close to the kids.

****

Waste not want not! For a few pence an old cardigan can be transformed into a splendid carrying-case for your laptop computer.

========

Dear 'Primrose',

Just because you're getting a bit long in the tooth is no excuse to compromise with bourgeois 'morality'. How on earth will women ever emancipate themselves fully from masculine dominion if they let themselves become 'squeamish' on such matters?!

§§§§§§§

Following our recent feature on hypothermia, readers of 'Age War' have sent in some other handy tips for keeping warm this winter:

* Setting fire to ex-junior-health ministers is a cheap and enjoyable source of heat.

* Listening to Robert Robinson on the wireless always works for me. A few minutes of that nauseous little toad wittering on to his ex-Oxbridge chums and I'm boiling with fury.

* As the government advises, buy a set of clothes secondhand, knit a colourful scarf and hat, then stuff the whole lot with newspaper, plonk it on a nearby street corner and see if you can't collect enough pennies in November to pay the heating bill till spring.

(((()))

Joe Sharrow wrote me a lovely card to say he and wife Hilda had a wonderful weekend in Dieppe though 'it was a bit drizzly' and suggests I hand on this useful tip which they tried out (successfully, I hasten to add!) on their return trip: to smuggle gin through customs simply fill up screw-top bottles of lemonade and keep them in your hand-luggage. Nice idea, Joe! And good luck with the hip replacement, Hilda!

+++++++

In reply to a long letter received from 'Confused' of Cheltenham:

1 No, with false teeth it's not advisable
2 A solution of salt and surgical spirit applied diligently every morning should help
3 Hegemony
4 Boxing gloves in bed should do the trick
5 He didn't really, did he?!
6 Perhaps a cricket bat would be more advisable.

&&&&&&&

A THOUGHT:

A friend in need is a friend indeed,
That's how the old adage goes.
And ne'er were a wiser word spoken I say,
and a rose is a rose is a rose.

Reprinted from *The Pensioner's Friend*

††††††††

Helen Arborthorne phoned the other day. I'm sure all our thoughts are with her at such a difficult time. But I do wish she wouldn't moan on so. Get out there and join an evening class or something, woman! She also informs me she met Bessie Mappin in Safeways last Wednesday who asked her to pass on to readers that Janice Ecclesall is expecting another child (her third) in September and hoping for no repetition of her wind problem this time. And says she'd quite like a girl but 'isn't too bothered either way', though why Bessie thought my readers might be interested in that is beyond me.

×××××××××

WISE WORDS INDEED

The sense of a proposition is its agreement and disagreement with possibilities of existence and non-existence of states of affairs.

Wittgenstein

00000000

Finally a kind letter from Fanny Kelvin in response to the sad news about Rusty, which I included in the last issue. She writes: 'Dear Maudie, Hope you're well and your knee's calmed down [it has at time of writing, thank you, Fanny dear!]. So sorry to hear about Rusty who was a real gent with a merry smile and always a kind word for everyone during the many happy years we spent as comrades together. So it came as a great shock to hear of him crossing picket lines during the recent housing department dispute which is tantamount to class treachery in my book. I popped into Griselda's for a cuppa last Friday and had a splendid time reminiscing about old Abortion Bill days and eating her lovely digestives . . . Whoops but I'm running out of space! More of Fanny's news next time! 'Bye now!

For Children of All Ages

Gavin Youngperson of the SPLAF Youth Wing's Parents, Live-In Lovers and Toddler Group takes a look at some new anti-ageist children's books for the old at heart.

My First Book of Hard Facts
by the Springwinter Co-operative

A beautifully illustrated book for the pre-school child which honestly and simply explains in clear, direct language that your child will understand:
* the iniquities of the British education system
* the patriarchal overtones of the Father Christmas myth
* the internal workings of a hand-held food blender
* what exactly it's like having your wisdom teeth pulled
* the chances of surviving a nuclear winter
* how, even though they seem to get on okay, statistics prove that mummy and daddy will probably be divorced quite soon
* that granny may well be a lesbian but frankly that's the least of your problems.

The Chronicles of Elderland
by Roald Dour

In which Tiffin, Snoggers, Wanky and Bumfluff, a gang of plucky young public schoolchildren, visiting their curious uncle for the summer hols, find a mysterious wardrobe, climb inside and find themselves trapped for the duration of the story.

Meanwhile, in the chest-of-drawers they failed to notice lies the entrance to a magic land of ancient white witches who live in perfect harmony, undisturbed.

The Old Wife's Tale
by Brenda Gleam

A pleasant, if somewhat predictable, tale of a king who promises the hand of his daughter in marriage to the first prince to kill the wicked witch. Prince Abdul fights ghosts, gremlins and institutional racism on his way to the witch who turns out to have a tremendously demanding day job as a hospital ancillary worker. She turns the handsome prince into a wholemeal bap, the princess falls in love with her, the bap sues for breach of contract but the witch forgives him all the same and turns him into a very charming old man and they all live as happily as is possible under a repressive feudal dictatorship. Good so far as it goes but why, oh why, no mention of people with learning difficulties?

The Puffin Book of the Dead

A fascinating anthology of stories which imaginatively introduce the notion of mortality to the younger reader. Including: Tintin and the Funeral Directors; In Which Pooh Bear Loses His Stuffing; Asterix and The Gall Bladder Operation; Mog Meets Her Maker; Heart Attack at Primrose Farm; Spot's Last Walk. Highly recommended.

OHO!
by Justin and Felicity Belsize

Here's an extract from the latest winner by the husband-and-wife team, featuring those lovable characters from *Poopoo! Kaka!* and *Woopsy!*

Once a little baby
A B C
peeps out of his buggy —
What does he see?

OHO!

He sees his Granny cooking
Cos Mummy's gone away,
Gran, as usual, helps out,
She's been ironing all day.

He sees her do the washing up
And cooking all the food,
Daddy drinking lager
To the television glued.

He hears his Daddy talking
To someone on the phone:
Dad says, 'Mum's getting past it,
Think I'll put her in a home!'

He sees his Daddy laughing,
But what does he see later?
Daddy kissing Gran good night,
The rotten two-faced traitor!

A Life in the Day in the Grannyflat of Betty Spital

I rise at six every morning in my Sheffield grannyflat, take a cup of weak tea to my bed and open the mail in this single room which is all that I have to call home during my autumn years. It may be small, but it suits my requirements. After all, I spent my childhood years in a back-to-back in sooty Spitalcliffe. I bought this open-plan, loft-style studio in '65. We at SPLAF were the vanguard of the sixties property boom. Oh, aye, in a non-revolutionary situation we believe in playing the system till the pips squeak!

It's grand to have a comfy chair when you're old and getting on a bit. I found this one in an empty house round the corner. It's a crime! There's ever such a lot of property left standing empty round here, while the owners are off on their skiing holidays.

Like all old people, I like to have my personal things about me – knick-knacks of sentimental value. Like this original Man Ray furry tea-cup and the bloodstained brick I keep as a memento of happy days in Grosvenor Square. That battered bakelite wireless set is my lifeline to the world. That and the cordless telephone, the hi-fi and the IBM clone word processor/computer terminal.[1]

Of course, it's hard on a state pension, surviving in the heartless, sink-or-swim society we've seen develop under Thatcherdom, but we pensioners pride ourselves on our resourcefulness, tha' knows.

Things have got a bit easier since SPLAF members were driven

---

1. Pensioners and New Technology (PANT) can be contacted c/o Floor 112, Mandela House, London W1.

to start a self-help Christmas Club Grapevine of us own.[1] No substitute for decent state provision, of course, but there we are . . . What happens is we pool our pensions and I gamble it all on bullion and gilts. It's a risky, hand-to-mouth existence. But so far we're up three million on the last quarter's trading, so we should think ourselves lucky, I expect.

And we all bought shares in British Gas. In fact, I gather we'll soon have a controlling interest. So we'll be threatening the city with another Big Bang shortly, if they don't cave in to our demands for SPLAF to sequestrate their pension funds.

1. Probably inspired by the working practice of Blackmail Therapy fully documented in Harris, S. and Harris, M., *I'm OK – You're Middle-Aged* (Denver, 1974). [Ed.]

Betty: *You've not asked me about my life's mission yet!*

CM: Betty, in a word, how would you sum up your life's mission?

Betty: *Oh, now, that's a tricky one. Well, of course, I've contributed so much as an activist, a muse, a politician, an artist . . .*

CM: Of course.

Betty: *But I suppose the key word is Communication. As little Mr Tse-tung used to say, 'Betty, the pen is mightier than the sword and far cheaper than air-to-ground missiles.' Word-spreading is so important. That's why I devote so much time*

to travelling the globe with my message of reassurance to the oppressed.

CM: And what message is that?

Betty: *That they should think themselves lucky they don't suffer as I do!*

CM: So, for what would you most like to be remembered?

Betty: *Making the best raspberry jam in South Yorkshire.*

CM: Is that all?

Betty: *Oh, and single-handedly changing the course of modern history.*

On the North–South Divide and Where They Can Shove It

The Grey Plaque Guide to London

Gavin drove me down to the station, settled me into a seat, stowed away my luggage and wheelchair, and waved me off on my latest excursion to a strife-torn trouble-spot. As disturbing as it can be investigating these areas of deprivation, I do think it so important that we fortunate folk witness these things first-hand.

Made it across the border with no difficulty. No sign of pass-port control yet at the North–South Divide. Arrived at my desti-nation 3.15 and, my god, it's depressing. Even the station is jampacked with starving itinerant sock, tie and croissant-sellers touting for trade.

The prices they charge to go on this fancy new Thameslink line are preposterous! Wonder if anyone ever pays them? On the platform at my destination I unfolded my wheelchair and climbed in. By the time the station manager had carted me single-handedly up and down all those stairs to the exit he was far too exhausted to think of asking for my ticket.

It's very seldom I visit London these days, but every once in a while I feel it my parental duty to go to my daughter's. I knew her and what'sisname were away in their cottage in the Algarve and I'd got my own set of keys cut last time I were down.

Honestly, the smug and patronizing way some people talk about those poor underprivileged yuppoes makes me sick. It's not their fault they can only get work in shady financial institutions and have to live in cramped little make-shift shelters by the side of the docks. I blame the schools. Sculling, fagging and wanking are all well and good, but no substitute for proper work-training.

Sometimes I feel ever so guilty about the way I brought up our Rosa. Perhaps it was wrong of me to disown her at three weeks to travel the world . . . But then all parents feel they got it wrong somewhere along the line, don't they? So I try not to dwell on it. Anyway, no amount of maternal deprivation gives a daughter the right to join the Conservatives.

Poky little place they've got in the Isle of Dogs. No food in the house. Just a lot of rotting meat in this big white box affair I disconnected when I arrived to make room for my wheelchair. Nothing to drink but water with bubbles in. At least, not now that I've polished off their wine cellar.

And the corner shop's obviously verging on bankruptcy. Fancy stocking nothing but different shapes of pasta! And they can't even afford to buy real tins of the stuff; they have to make it themselves on the premises!

Rosa and Thingy must have run out of paint when they decorated. Been reduced to rubbing the leftovers on to the wall with a sponge. I couldn't stand to think of them living there with it looking like that, so I painted the whole place again properly tonight in this peculiar browny-green shade they were selling off cheap down the road. I think it's an awful colour, so ten to one they'll love it.

Now I'm exhausted and ready for bed. The trouble is I've searched high and low and can find no sign of one. I'll have to make do with the old mattress on two wooden pallets they keep in their room.

It's always seemed to me a terrible flaw in British culture that, unlike most other countries, there's only one major city in Britain where the quality of life is so far advanced from the rest that the others are left standing. I gather Glasgow's catching up, but in general it's shocking how Sheffocentrist our view of the world has become.

It can't be said that London doesn't make the most of what benefits it's got. Quite endearing what a hoo-ha it makes about a few beefeaters and a palace. But you can tell a place is pretty desperate for tourist attractions when it can't think of anything better to sell as souvenirs than reproduction street signs and models of buses.

They try hard, but the absence here of really world-class snooker players, decent municipal socialism and dogshit-free parks is depressingly apparent. I know I'm as guilty as the rest of us of forgetting that there's more to life than gets reported in the Sheffield *Star*. Though I couldn't find much sign of it here, frankly.

The social services down here these days are despicable. This morning I visited a huge, draughty building where old people still congregate in cold weather to drink and snooze. I thought they'd sold off all these crumbling Victorian institutions long ago, but the House of Lords remains unchanged.

Popped in to the Other Place and ate my sandwiches in the visitors' gallery, ogling Ken Livingstone. God, that man's sexy! Oh, to be seventy again! They chucked me out, though. Well, nobody told me you had to be a member to heckle.

Chatted with Tony (Benn) in his office after. But you can't have a decent conversation with him these days; he keeps breaking off to write it up for his diary. Makes a fine cup of tea still, though. Then, on with my travels. The tube trains are so inefficient and unfriendly. We got stuck in the tunnel at one point and everyone was so quiet and miserable that I tried to cheer up my neighbour by telling her my experiences of the Sheffield Blitz. She just ignored me, went horribly pale and literally bolted out of the doors when we finally got to King's Cross.

Found I'd run out of cash, so popped into this place called the South Bank and spent a frustrating hour looking for a cashpoint. Eventually had to borrow a tenner off a lass I spotted there who once played the fairy in panto at the Crucible; a good little earner that, Equity minimum for saying 'You shall go to the ball!' once a night and getting to wear all those sequins and feathers. You should see the amount of lines she has to memorize now, and all

122

to wear glorified sack-cloth in some secondhand play. Written by a dead man apparently, which seems rather macabre.

Just time for a spot of window-shopping in Regent Street. On my pension window-shopping's all I can afford. You get the shop assistants scrabbling about in the window display, fetching you things they haven't got left in stock, thus leaving you unobserved long enough to stuff a few other items in your hold-all. Actually, there's not much in the shops here you can't get in Sheffield. Every city you visit these days has a shopping precinct exactly like the one back home. But then plagiarism is the highest form of flattery.

Then on to Highgate Cemetery for the real reason for my London visit. I always like to pop in on Karl on his birthday. Brought him some flowers as usual and gave him a kiss on those big bronze lips of his. Call me a sentimental old drip if you like, but I feel so sorry for the old bugger, buried down here in the back of the Tory beyond.

Artburn Manifesto

Statement of Intent written jointly by members of the Spitalcliffe Sunday Sketching Group

1 We Grannies Glow and Glory in the face of the abuse of the Yunksters of Junk Culture; we are Wrinklies, Wraucous, Wrathful and Wraving; we are O.A.P.s: Open, Angry and Proudly Painting!

2 All art which refuses to acknowledge the existence of pensioners is by its very nature babyish and immature.[1]

3 Our self-styled teacher calls us short-sighted; we call ourselves the Neo-Impressionists. Only with our glasses off can we see beyond middle-age/class/brow definitions to the cosmic fuzziness beyond.

4 Teacher says: 'Not bad for someone your age, dear.' We say: 'Go shove it up your critical faculty, yunk scum!'

5 Marx says: 'I have sown dragon's teeth and harvested fleas.' We Twerlies say: 'We have urinated On Golden Pond and poisoned the slugs.'

6 We spurn your empty abstractions! We laugh at your lame landscapes, hollow ikons to the god of private property! We cry: 'Death to your life classes, purveyors of painterly porn!'

7 We reiterate: the Still Life is the Only Fitting Subject Matter for Authentic Community Artists of the Dawning Third Age!

---

1. In a certain form and to a certain extent.

The First Twerly Art Show
at the Mappin Art Gallery

Introduction to the Catalogue by Sir Hugh Psalter

Polyfilla as a medium violates our expectations: swirls of sea-shells embedded in its pitted surface evoke the potent Venus myth, and the Chianti bottle it encases conjures up a plethora of Bacchanalian antecedents. Balanced resplendent atop this deceptively grotesque construction sits a sculpture, part metaphor of political activity in old age, part misshapen attempt at a raffia lampshade, which acts as keynote to this ground-breaking exhibition.

Concepts of time, dimensionality and moral order are also clearly apparent in A. Glossop's exquisite series 'Shoe-brush Tidies I to IX'. Bravura explosions of clashing patterns of sticky-backed plastic equivocate between emotional stridency and a more contemplative debate concerning the play between chaos and regimentation in the modern world.

The surface dullness of 'Piece of Paper Blu-tac'ed to Wall with the Words: Tea & Coffee 20p per Cup Written on It in Biro' by Arnold Bendibus masks a near-literary intentionality. And recent feminist critical re-evaluation of the aesthetic content of knitted garments gives added poignancy to 'Socks', an arabesque of multi-hued foot protection.

But it is the richly variegated orgy of textures to be found amongst the serried ranks of second-hand clothes that B. Spital arranges in a maze-like assemblage of hangers and poles which exudes perhaps the greatest resonance.

Near by stands a flat, minimalist oblong of laminated chipboard, ingeniously held aloft by slender, polished steel columns at each of its four corners and covered with a menagerie of broodingly menacing misshapen furry toys.

In B. Spital's powerful performance piece 'Old Lady Shouting Bog Off You Pretentious Wanker to Drunk Critic', the artist makes a dramatic and intensely painful plea for her work to be excluded from what she sees as the limiting definitions of conventional art categorization.

And yet it must be said that this show, a bold attempt to challenge traditional notions of the role of art in everyday life by attracting new audiences to galleries through their use as venues for jumble sales, may once again be undermined by contextualization within an art-historical catalogue introduction of staggeringly pretentious vacuity.

In conversation with Ms Spital, she firmly denied a Duchampian influence:
'Marcel Duchamp? He did visit the Spitalcliffe Sunday Sketching Group once to give us a little slide-show. I caught him in our local after trying to sneak out with a urinal from the Gents stuffed up his smock.

'I may not know much about art, but I know what I loathe and despise.

'Dada, my aunt fanny! A dirty toilet is about as surreal as the furry tea cup Arnold Bendibus gave me to keep my cocoa warm in winter!

'As I told Tristan Tzara, "Dada is this. Dada is that. Dada is shit. Gaga is best." '

The Case of Fraulein
Betty S.[1]

I was quietly at work in my consulting-room one morning, making some preliminary notes for a new edition of my study of jokes and their relation to the unconscious, when there came a loud knocking at the door. I inquired from whom the sound emanated.

'Betty,' came the reply.

'Betty, who?' I asked.

'Bet he'll wish he never asked!' cried a young woman, who burst into the room displaying a variety of most unusual neurotic symptoms. Although young, curiously attractive and apparently physically fit, she was hunched at the shoulders and shuffling slowly with the support of a walking-stick. Her lips were drawn downwards in a dour expression, whilst through gritted teeth she muttered unintelligibly.

Lying down with some difficulty upon the couch, the young woman explained that I had been recommended to her by a colleague of mine in the psychoanalytic fraternity. Betty was on a cycling tour round Europe jointly sponsored by the International Peace Movement and her local Trades Council, handing out lapel badges bearing the inscription: SAY NO TO NAZISM — SAY YES TO PILKINGTON'S RELISH. She was determined to visit Berlin where she aimed to avert world war by persuading Adolf Hitler that his fine contribution to the art of house-painting was of far greater significance than anything he could possibly achieve in the political arena, but the progress of her mission had been

1. From Freud, S., *Civilisation and Its Incontinents, Complete Works* Vol.XXV (London 1953–74).

impeded by the development of these extraordinary symptoms for which she could find no medical explanation.

I have to say that my professional curiosity was immediately aroused as for many years I had been convinced of the existence of such a neurosis, which I had already characterized as 'geronto-somatic', that is, caused by a deep-rooted jealousy of the old on the part of those youngsters resentful of the pressures upon them to take part in the gruelling rounds of parties and other social engagements and so wishing subconsciously that they were, in Goethe's words, *zu müd' zur Lust*.[1]

Up until that time, I had no first-hand evidence of such 'tomb envy' to substantiate my hypothesis, though rumours had reached me of youngsters dressing as old ladies in an attempt to procure senior citizen savercards under false pretences.

At this point, I put the patient into a state of mild hypnosis by placing my hands on her head and asked B. what she thought of her libido. She replied that she never swam there because it was too cold and she knew local boys urinated in it. I questioned her on her sexual history and the frank account she gave led me to doubt my belief that all human behaviour is founded on sexual repression. Surely this enticing young creature could have no unenacted desires left to repress!

Then I placed my hands on her breasts and noted that my scientific career was in serious jeopardy . . .

Now, of course, since my work has achieved a certain notoriety, I have frequently been visited by wealthy Viennese ladies titillated by the gross parodies of my theories as represented in the popular press who, under the subterfuge of feigned mental illness, wish only to flirt with the man whose name is these days synonymous with all things naughty and daring. But up to now I have had little problem in recognizing and dealing with such wily charlatans and repressing the mildly erotic impulses their coquettish behaviour generated in myself.

With this young woman it was different. In a trice we had torn off our clothes and flung ourselves down on the couch. At the

1. Too pooped to pop.

end of a lengthy and probing consultation, I noted that Betty was beaming from ear to ear, singing gaily and moving like any normal girl her age.

What else could explain her miraculous cure but the regenerative powers of my sexual prowess? A possibility which opened up exciting new avenues for therapeutic methodology.

However, Betty herself had a different interpretation for what had occurred. She admitted that for many years she had felt profoundly oppressed by the pervasive presence in art and architecture of those symbols of male mastery and control which in my work I explained were modelled subconsciously upon the shape of the phallus erect. Finding that the organ which inspired my insight looked, as she put it, 'less like a towering monument to male supremacy than a raw chipolata', had at a stroke freed her from all morbid fears of masculine domination.

At the end of the consultation I noted an interesting Freudian slip of my own when instead of saying, as usual, 'Good-bye and good luck, Fraulein', I found myself sobbing like a baby and howling 'I want my mummy!'

Postscript

In the weeks that followed this meeting, Freud sought consolation by burying himself in work on the formulation of the Super-Oedipal Complex, whereby grandparental repression of the desire to copulate with their offspring results in neurotic compulsions to knit them ill-fitting pullovers instead.

On Censorship

Why, oh why, must the decent citizens of this great country of ours be subjected night after night to the torrent of vile filth and putrid propaganda which pours out of our television sets in a constant stream of nauseating bile, courtesy of those pea-brained subversives at the self-styled British Broadcasting Corporation and its evil partner in crime, the IBA?

And what, oh what, is to become of us now that the Satellite Revolution threatens to inundate us entirely (and especially the housebound) in slimy, stinking yuck?

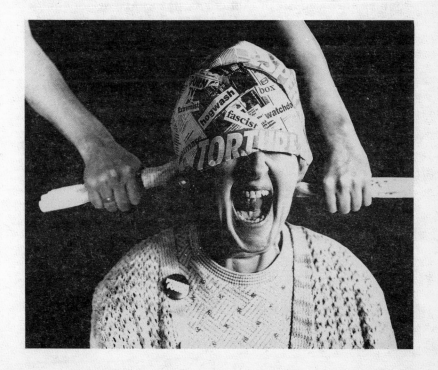

Believe me, I'm 101 per cent behind any attempts to muzzle these drossmongers.

However, we in SPLAF's new media watchdog working-party would beg to differ ever so slightly with Sir William Rees-Mogg and his associates on the grounds on which decisions are made about what's to be banned.

Censorship is an ugly word. As young Duncan Campbell was saying to me on the phone last week (ever such a nice boy he is, but terribly paranoid), 'Betty, our freedom of speech is in jeopardy. These days the media gets pounced on by the authorities just for talking about . . .' We were cut off; I got a cross-line with Menwith Hill.

We take it as read that in any democratic society the inalienable right of the adult human being to complete freedom of information through the press and broadcast media must be sacrosanct.

But numskulls dumb enough to vote Thatcher back three times running are obviously in a different category. These poor unfortunates cannot be relied upon to think for themselves and need all the help they can get from elders and betters to reshape their brains to near-normal proportions. It's up to us, Comrade Elderpeople!

Several areas worry us in particular:

CHILDREN'S PROGRAMMES: All this senseless violence. When I baby-sit our Tracey's little brats, I'm appalled at these so-called Children's Programmes making killing people look like fun. If they must show violence to kids then show them the real thing: Super Ted fighting state brutality in China, Thundercats against apartheid. Tell it to them how it is; kids need to learn about these things early, before they've had the ideological analysis knocked out of 'em at school.

SEX: To my mind, it should be banned completely after nine o'clock. It's disgusting, all this cheap titillation for sexist, lecherous middle-aged men. They should show the sex in the daytime when sensible people, housewives, children and pensioners, are watching; them as can enjoy a bit of arousal without getting oppressive about it.

DOCUMENTARY DRAMA: Social conscience is all very well, but I do think they go too far with these short films they're forever running about society's unfortunates. It can be most distressing for an old person settling down to their evening meal to be confronted by sick perverts with fetishes about instant coffee and bars of chocolate, people who get their sexual kicks from fondling gear levers or sticking bits of plastic into slots in banks. Most heartbreaking of all is that poor family whose house is apparently so over-mortgaged that they can only afford trite banter and Oxo cubes for their tea.

In particular, the following programmes we would have no choice but to ban completely:

ANTIQUES ROADSHOW: Promotes a negative view of old age as a commodity to be sold off for private gain.

THE BILL: Politically biased. Promotes the image of policemen as tough, sometimes brutal, but at heart basically normal human beings with a difficult and essential job to do.

EASTENDERS: I lost all hope for it after they killed off Gran.

HIGHWAY: Encourages religious mania and tone-deafness amongst the old.

LAST OF THE SUMMER WINE: Nostalgia-sodden claptrap.

THE LAST RESORT: Promotes negative image of people with speech impediments.

THE MONEY PROGRAMME: Obscene.

SPITTING IMAGE: Politically biased. They've obviously succumbed to Home Office pressure not to make a puppet of me.

POINTS OF VIEW: I just don't like it.

WOGAN: Promotes negative stereotype of Irishmen as vacuous, egocentric smarmpots.

However, don't for one moment think of the role of our Watchdog Team as being in any way negative. British Television is still the best in the world we're proud to say and there are plenty of nice, well-made, quality shows to be seen on our screens which we wouldn't dream of scrapping if they were prepared to make the alterations recommended by our own script unit, which has already started to bombard the TV companies with complaints, threats and handy tips.

'Blind Date' has always seemed to me to be a harmless bit of fun, and I have noted with pleasure Cilla's well-intentioned moves to pair off oldsters as well as young. But surely these popular shows could serve an educational purpose as well as a recreational one? For instance:

CILLA: Well, Freda, you've got a tricky choice with three gorgeous guys to choose from. What's yer first question darling?

FREDA: I think I'll start with Number 3. Number 3, would you agree with Karl Marx that of all the instruments of production, the greatest productive force is the revolutionary class itself and that the organization of the revolutionary elements as a class presupposes the existence of all the productive forces that could be engendered in the womb of the old society?

DYNASTY and DALLAS are refreshing both for their perspicacious analysis of the underlying nature of human relations within the capitalist system (the Richer the Shittier) and the frequency with which they depict elderly people enjoying sexual activity. However, we would seek to inject a bit more realism:

BLAKE: I love you, son. I love you. You know I do. And you know as sure as I'm standing here that I'd do anything within my power to win back control of the Company for my own flesh and blood. I'd do anything to have my revenge on that scheming hussy! But my back's been playing me up something rotten lately and my bunions are murder. Can't it wait till tomorrow?

ADAM: Father, I want that Company and I want it now! (*Downs his whisky and leaves.*)

BLAKE: (*picking up telephone*): Andrex?

SECRETARY: Yes, Mister Carrington?

BLAKE: Put a call through to my chiropodist, will ya, and fast!

Personally I must admit to being rather hooked on 'Neighbours', though I do find those drawling Birmingham accents a trifle grating. And the plot lines could do with pepping up a bit.

134

SCOTT: Hiya, wifey. I'm home! Phew, I'm fair tuckered out. Been picketing the café for refusing to serve abos!

MRS MANGLE: Hello there, Scott.

SCOTT: Mrs Mangle! G'day! Whatcha doing with your hands up Charlene's jumper?

MRS MANGLE: Just measuring her up for a bra. Wasn't I, dear?

Our message to the media is clear: WHY, FOR CRYING OUT LOUD, CAN'T THEY SHOW MORE PROGRAMMES ORDINARY OLD-FOLK CAN RELATE TO? Why on earth can't we once in a while have a nice, decent programme about radical pensioners plotting the violent overthrow of western capitalism?

Actually, we at SPLAF are so pig sick of what's on offer that we're planning to do our own thing and start a little satellite TV channel of our own. At the moment we're still having teething problems with the highly specialized technology involved. I've had a Pyrex serving-dish strapped to the roof of my flatlet for months now and can't even pick up Sky Channel.

We have plenty of programme ideas tucked up our cardies. For instance:

MOTHER-IN-LAW: A fun game-show for all the family in which mums compete for the prize of dropping Bernard Manning into a vat of stale vomit.

HOSPICE: A thrilling soap opera which would offer cameo roles to many elderly Equity members in need of a career boost.

PRO-CELEBRITY SUMO WRESTLING: The ideal sport for the armchair hooligan.

STRIPAGRAN: Mixing sex games, hints on benefits and clips from 'Come Dancing' to create the ultimate in low-budget adult entertainment for the very mature.

Betty holding up half the sky

Travels with the Diplomatic Bag
The World According to SPLAF

As SPLAF's Diplomatic Envoy Overseas, Betty Spital has carved a unique niche for herself as walk-on actor *par excellence* on the contemporary world stage. 'The Elder Statesmen's Elderly Stateswoman' is no stranger to jet-lag or travel-sickness as she flits between time zones in her quest to press the pensioners' case wherever relevant or not.

Betty Spital speaks only one language fluently, but that extremely loudly. Her international network of grandmothers of the famous and cleaners of the corridors of power keep her up to the minute on the-news-behind-the-news. She enjoys relations with many senior politicians of our day over whom she has been said to have a Rasputinesque hold.

Recent terrorist outrages and the resultant tightening of airport security have considerably restricted Betty's access to her preferred mode of economy-class travel in aeroplane luggage bays. These days she either posts herself second class to penfriends abroad or, ever abreast of current trends, seeks business sponsorship to fund her travels: multinational drug syndicates have proved especially eager to offer financial support in exchange for a few simple errands. Thankfully the Little Old Lady behind the great men and women of contemporary politics continues to be a familiar sight in departure lounges and duty-free shops worldwide.

[Ed.]

The World According to SPLAF

Pour those as ne me connaissez pas, je suis Eurotwerly und SPLAF delegate at this year's Pensioners' Internationale to be held in the Soviet Union. Nice spot we've got for it this time: Sheffield's twin city of Blunketgrad, just next door to Chernobyl. Ever so quiet and remarkable weather for the time of year.

I'm not a great one for summits, me – I prefer deeds to words – but these SAGA cruises are so cheap at the moment and I fancied having another quick peek at the planet before I go. Or it goes, whichever's first.

We've got a packed agenda:

1 APARTHEID

The SPLAF campaign of harassment of greengrocers stocking South African produce is beginning to bite. This involves our members fiddling about with their purses at check-outs, fingering fragile items, keeping the queue waiting by telling the shop assistant about our Shirley's hysterectomy and surreptitiously affixing PRODUCE OF CHERNOBYL stickers to fruit and vegetable stocks.

However, we are still unwilling to impose sanctions. We feel that our original plan to call on pensioners to refuse to buy any goods from British shops until either Thatcher takes firm action against apartheid or we starve to death in protest may only hurt those we aim to support.

For the time being we continue to demand the severance of all links between white British Grannies and any traitorous relations of theirs resident in that evil empire.

We will also boycott all attempts to hold the World Pensioners' Games in Natal.

2 NUCLEAR DISARMAMENT

Detente and multilateral peace agreements are all for the best, I suppose, but when you get to my age the thought of imminent nuclear catastrophe can be a great source of comfort. Reassuring to think I'll see things through to the very end. No one'll get the chance to slag me off after *my* funeral. We'll all go together when we go.

3 THE EEC

We at SPLAF are totally opposed to the opening of the single European Market in 1992.

In the old days our little corner shop had everything you could possibly require. Now already you can walk for miles in one of these bloody megastore places and still no sight nor sound of corn plasters.

4 THE MIDDLE EAST

I do wish people would learn to keep religion out of politics. It makes things so unnecessarily complicated. How are you supposed to work out which side are the goodies? As Che Guevara used to say, 'Give me a good old-fashioned class conflict any day!'

5 THE THIRD WORLD

A lot of people in this country think of the Third World as nothing but a place full of famines and tinpot dictators. These pathetically ignorant, stereotyped notions are just typical of the blinkered insularity of the people of these islands.

I'm sure it's not like that at all.

6 RUSSIA AND AMERICA

I spent a weekend in Moscow on my way here. It was terribly kind of the Gorbachevs to put me up. But, after all, I have been close to Mikhail for years. He and I were engaging in Heavy Perestroika underneath the iron duvet way back in the McCarthy era. Before he met his dear wife, Ryvita, I hasten to add.

I glasnosted with them all in my heyday. As Nikita Khrushchev was so fond of saying, 'Bettinka, it may be cold war outside, but in my heart it's spring.'

Mikhail was very keen to hear what I thought of George Bush.

'Micky,' I said to him, 'not a lot, to be honest. But it's that jumped-up *nouveau* twerlie wife of his I really can't stand.'

Frankly I preferred Reagan. Ron may be an imperialist, he may be militaristic, clumsy, stupid and full of baloney, but he does have one thing in his favour. He is very, very old. No one that old can be all bad.

Nice to be back in the USSR. Reminds me of old days, when it were Blunt and Burgess, Spital and Maclean. 'The fourth man' they used to call me. Sexist pigs!

7 CHINA

It hurts me down deep to have to side with young students against elderly Stalinists, but there's no getting round it: those poor democracy campaigners acted with the idealism and bravery of people three times their age.

Methuselah Unchained

A Prophecy by William Bakewell[1]

Spitahl[2] *roars and shakes her stick in the wrathful air,*
Infecting with her venom th'elders' brains.
The curse of Bakewell falls on Satan's lair;[3]
Still no one's been around t'unblock my drains.

GOWNA[4] *prattles on to busty hussies,*[5]
Neighbours of the prophet gripe and grass,
The dogs unchained jet forth their urine freely,[6]
Yea verily the things of which I speak shall come to pass –

Th'Almighty comes at last to wicked Spitalcliffe
And on the pervert invert commie scum shalt vent his spleen
Bringing pestilence and plague to Steel City
And Dead Ringer romping home at 3.15.[7]

1. William Bakewell, ex-serviceman and retired road-sweeper, was a faithful, if unremarkable, member of SPLAF until visited one evening by the Angel Gabriel – in the form of a door-to-door salesman on behalf of the blind – who inadvertently revealed to him his godhead and sold him a yellow anti-static LP duster, now held as a holy relic by members of the Geriatrics of God, the small cult religion (well, tiny, actually) spawned by Bakewell's oeuvre.

From that moment on, Bakewell's beliefs swerved violently to the right and he took full-time to scribbling prophetic visions on the back of old betting-slips which he either posts to the local paper or Sellotapes to the wall of the phone box at the end of his road.

2. In Bakewell's complex cosmology Spitahl ranks alongside Ken Livingstone and Fiona Stannington (barmaid at the Crown) in the minions of the Antichrist.

3. Obscure. Either Colonel Gaddafi or Sheffield City Council's Chief Cleansing Officer.

4. An anagram of WOGAN.

5. It is on the question of sexual politics that he and Ms Spital are most divided. Whereas Betty believes in absolute equality between women and those she affectionately calls 'The Dickheads', Bakewell is convinced that a woman's place is on all-fours in a cut-away rubber wetsuit being chastised with a rolled-up copy of the *Sporting Times*.

Only from this position can she have any chance of catching the eye of the Almighty whom, Bakewell informs us, 'gets off on that kind of stuff'. His attitude to the afterlife is more egalitarian: in his own words on the occasion of his de-selection from the SPLAF finance committee, 'You can all go to hell.' But, ever-forgiving, Betty still welcomes his presence at meetings.

6. The details of the protracted court case this refers to are still *sub judice*.

7. Spital's tolerant attitude towards such a deranged old fascist may be explained by the unerring accuracy of Bakewell's racing tips. Dead Ringer (100–1) did indeed win by a length that week at Haydock Park.

Betty's Christmas Message[1]

Dear Comrades,

Just a quick note to send the traditional greetings of the season from your old friend Betty Spital, revolutionary pensioner, retired urban terrorist and, when all's said and done, a mum.

Christmas is a wonderful time of year for us; our chance to visit our offspring, to sit round the yuletide tree with all our sons, daughters and grandchildren gathered around us.

Where would the SPLAF campaign for the destruction of the nuclear family be without Christmas?

Did you get your Xmas shopping done in time? Well, I say 'shopping'. Christmas is a magical time of year for us shoplifters. I've got my present lover, Gavin, a lovely willy-warmer: 'For the anti-sexist man with everything'. When the wearer gets sexually aroused a warning-light flashes and it plays a medley of Joan Armatrading hits.

Cousin Stan asked for a bottle of scotch, as usual. I've got him the cartoon version of *Das Kapital*. Our Tracey wanted some frilly underwear. Bought her a *Spare Rib* diary.

---

1. Sending personalized Christmas cards became impossible for Betty when eye trouble developed the year after her shopping trip to Toxteth. The effects of the tear-gas were short-lived. History is grateful that a lasting consequence of this temporary, yet traumatic, disablement was the institution of Spital's annual Xmas missive. This started life as a simple mimeographed sheet sent to a small circle of friends and family. Currently published on video tape, audio tape, floppy disc, telex and fax, as well as the more conventional greetings card format, her ever-popular festive diatribe is sent to an exhaustive international mailing list of lonely pensioners, key world figures, fashion editors and political commentators.

[Ed.]

And my daughter Rosa, her as ratted on her class and married a dickhead from Surrey . . . After all, Christmas *is* Christmas. I've ordered her an enormous hamper from Harrods. Well, I'd pinched her husband's Barclaycard, so I thought 'Why not?'

I'll be alone in my little sheltered flatlet this Christmas. A quiet day – a slice or two of turkey, perhaps a cold mince pie and a glass of sherry. My old friend Doris Bendibus plans to pop in for a game of Scrabble, then it's a quick bath and off to bed.

Spare a thought for the elderly, enjoying cunnilingus in my new jacuzzi.

Festive greetings, Comrades.
Yours in struggle,

Ms B. Spital

The Prison Diaries of Betty Spital

Open Letter to: the U.N., Amnesty International, Fellow Political Prisoners Everywhere, All World Media
c/o Doris Bendibus, 8 Blunkett Lane, S2

Dear Doris & Co.

When first I was led by my interrogators into this small, confined space, when I heard the iron door slam shut, the key turn in the lock and the footsteps of my custodians fade away, I was determined they would never break me down.

How deeply moved I was to think of my supporters rallying round to organize torchlit vigils, prayer meetings, televised brass band concerts to be broadcast round the globe, demanding my release. At least I assume by now Mister Geldof will have been informed and started to get the ball rolling.

I well realized how my example of dignified bravery in the face of incarceration would be transmitted, like a beacon of hope, to all my fellow prisoners of conscience in dictatorial regimes worldwide.

But to be honest, I don't think I can take much more of this. Minute by minute, I feel the maltreatment taking its toll of my frail, weary body. Even the most heroic crusaders in the battle for human rights have their breaking-point. And two hours in police custody with nothing to eat or drink but a mouldy Kitkat and a cup of lukewarm Maxpax is mine.

Thrown into jail on a trumped-up charge and left to rot. Good gracious, if they call that disorderly conduct, they should have seen Vera by the end of that benefit knees-up we had for the ITV Grannython!

I can't abide the sight of these stone walls and iron bars – like a cage they are. Which reminds me: what was it Oscar Wilde said? Summat about handbags and Victoria Station? Not relevant, really.

I know what my supporters beyond these walls will be so concerned about. Have I endured police brutality? Have I been abused, beaten, starved, tortured for no crime whatsoever, but merely for remaining true to my deeply held political beliefs? Not yet, but I caught a vicious glint in the eye of that desk sergeant when I rubbed the fingerprint pad all down his clean shirt.

And the conditions in here are diabolical. You'd think we were back in Victorian times what with the hard toilet paper and no reading matter, bar back copies of *People's Friend*.

A free country, they call it. Free? 50p I had to pay for the sachet of liver salts I asked the constable to pop out to the chemist to get me and I've seen the double-size on offer for 95p at the market. But I did demand my right to one free phone call. Rang my friend Brenda who's out in Sydney, Australia, at present, visiting her Hazel. We chatted for hours.

They say you've got freedom of speech in this country. But what's the point of that? Why waste your breath in rhetorical oratory when everyone just barges past your soapbox to get to M & S? Free speech is all very well, but they should force folk to listen.

I'm in here on a completely bogus charge.

I've had this terrible head cold, see, and that was causing my insomnia to flare up, see, and when that happens the only way I can get off to sleep is to wear myself out first with a few good stiff whiskies and a brisk night-time stroll. And I thought while I'm out on the streets at this time of night I may as well do a spot of fly-posting – we're putting stickers on beer ads saying ALL MEN ARE POTENTIAL PENSIONERS as our bit for Age Awareness Week – and so I borrowed this Ford Sierra as was parked round the corner doing nowt useful, so I wouldn't have to hump heavy posters about. And I'd only just got out of the car to start work after a terrible experience with a dangerous pedestrian who came belting out of his front door without any hand signals whatsoever, causing me to crash into this pillar-box, when a copper came up and arrested me. For glue-sniffing.

BETTY SPITAL IS INNOCENT! All I did was sneeze and then blow my nose with the hanky I'd been using to wipe on the superglu!

Yours in solidarity,

Betty X

P.S. I SHALL BE RELEASED!
P.P.S. In about half an hour by the looks of things, Dolly, so be outside to meet me with a cardigan, won't you, dear.

The Perfumed Air-Freshener
An adult manual of sensual fulfilment
Concerning Everything That is Favourable about the
State of Being in Bed

Birds may do it, bees may do it, even educated fleas may bloody well do it, but people over retirement age aren't supposed to, oh no! Love amongst the elderly still dare not speak its name too loud for fear of shocking the hypocritical, satin-flesh-obsessed juvophile prudes we so wrongheadedly chose to procreate with our now-reviled organs of generation in the days when they still generated.

At least there exists a commonly accepted term for elderly gents of a sexual disposition, even if it is 'Dirty Old Men'. Old women, be they spinsters, wives or widows, aren't even credited with a little bit of smut.

Well, the tables are turning. It won't be long before no one under sixty will dare to have sex for fear they'll catch terminal ignorance and only those on their last legs already will risk getting a leg over or having a leg got over them.

We've all heard of young women complaining of unwanted sexual advances from the male sex, and good on them. But there are plenty of unwanted elderwomen equally complaining of male retreats. For many women, old age brings with it the sorrow of losing a much-loved partner after a long and blissful marriage to a devoted and caring man. Although now I see that written down in black and white, it does sound a bit unlikely.

Certainly it can take time to adjust to no longer having regular access to the intense physical pleasure of a good row over who's

hogging the duvet, or the warm intimacy of your soul-mate fart-
ing and snorting all night long beside you.

Hence the importance of clear, frank, no-holds-barred coun-
selling about . . . Well, you know what I mean. And a reminder
of some of the many other joys of bed beyond wedlock.

After all, sex can be terribly overrated. We all know that feeling, don't we, ladies, during a night spent in every conceivable
position for passionate carnal embrace with some gorgeous hot-
tongued young stud bringing us again and again to undreamt of
peaks of orgasmic crescendo, when we find ourselves lying there
thinking 'Perhaps I'd have been better off with a nice Agatha
Christie and the World Service?'

As mi mam used to say to us girls, 'There are parts of a woman
no virile member can reach.'

Sundry terms for the Mug of Hot Chocolate

El Snuzzo: The sender to sleep
El Milki: The one with the skin on top
El Koko: The lumpy one
El Whautri: The just-add-water variety
El Shuggri: The sweet one
El Auvultin: The one that tastes of soggy cardboard
El Dyjestiv Dunkhdin: The ultimate ecstasy

Concerning the Bringers of Inner Heat

Manner the 1st (The Rubber One): The woman introduces the
hot-water bottle between her thighs, then slowly pushes it
down her body until it reaches her toes, where it rests till the
water grows cold and she kicks it out of bed altogether.
Manner the 2nd (The Shocker): The man places himself on his
side, pulling his knees up so that his buttocks are raised. He
rests his head on his hands and falls deeply asleep. The woman,
having stayed up to watch the late movie, snuggles up beside

Stills from the movie Aya No Koko (I am Curious Gladys)

him and slips her ice-cold hands between his thighs to warm them directly upon his genital region.

Manner the 3rd (The Electric One): The woman bends down over the edge of the bed so that her buttocks are raised. She presses her breasts against the sheets and fiddles about down the side of the bed nearest the wall till she finds the switch on the electric blanket. Then she pops downstairs to catch the end of the movie while it heats up.

Manner the 4th (The Imagined One): The woman or man lies alone in bed fondling their sexual organs whilst reading the erotic literature of their choice. *Playlady*, *New Fetishist*, a good bodice-ripper or seed catalogue all work wonders for me.

Concerning Literature of the Erotic Variety

The issue of pornography and the pensioner is of course still something of a hot potato in elderly women's movement circles. The recent spate of books of erotica written by and for women inspired Doris Bendibus to have a crack at the genre herself:

'It's enormous!' Vera cried. 'I've never seen one so big!'

'Yes,' said the handsome young doctor, fingering it eagerly. 'And it's full of hot, steaming liquid just for you.'

With a groan of tenderness, he bent down towards her as she lay defenceless on the bed. Vera felt the warmth rush through her aching flesh as with firm, inquiring fingers he pulled back her skimpy cardigan to place the hot-water bottle beneath her throbbing neck.

'Wait there, my angel, while I go slip into something more comfortable,' he whispered huskily. In a trice he was back, clad in a nice V-necked sweater and a most attractive pair of bri-nylon slacks . . .

Sundry Cures for Sexual Dysfunction

In later life, many men find it hard to achieve or maintain an erection. In most cases this can easily be overcome if his partner is prepared to discuss the matter in a caring and supportive way, offer to give him arousing body massages and patiently coax his inert member back to life with a programme of licking, stroking and biting exercises employed gradually over the weeks, while the male lies supine.

On the other hand, she could always ditch him and go off with the milkman.

CM: Ms Spital, for someone of your age it must be hard not to dwell on . . . what's in store.

Betty: *The collapse of Capitalism, and the coming Revolution of the Glorious Third Age? Oh, I'm looking forward to it, blossom!*

CM: I mean . . . your death.

Betty: *Only slightly in the left ear.*

CM: Let me put it another way. Do you believe, at all, in an afterlife?

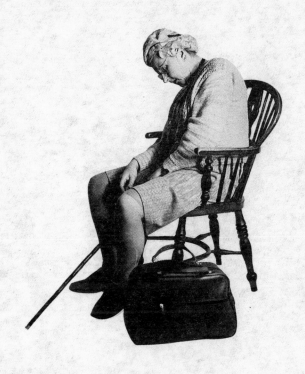

Betty: *Karl Marx used to say 'Religion is the opium of the people.' 'Karl,' I'd say to him, 'don't talk balls.'*

CM: So you believe in God?

Betty: *Oh, he exists all right, and it's our duty to work to over-throw the reactionary, dictatorial, patronizing bastard as soon as possible on our arrival in the afterlife, and replace him with a democratically elected Committee of the So-Called Damned!*

Twerly Park

A Proposal to Sheffield City Council Urban Regeneration Sub-Committee from SPLAF Heritage Think-Tank

As Councillors will be aware, Spitalcliffe Old People's Home is threatened with closure. In line with SPLAF's adoption of the policy of New Magic Realism, we intend not to mount a traditional campaign against cruel injustice but to adopt a more tactical approach to righting this wrong.

Following the success of such new leisure facilities as the Wigan Pier museum, where actors impersonate figures from working-class history, or the Museum of the Moving Image on the South Bank, which allows visitors to participate in reading the news etc., the SPLAF Heritage Think-Tank has come up with an idea for a scheme which would stimulate the local economy, boost party funds and at the same time offer amusement and important political re-education to the junior age groups in our society.

In consultation with top gerontologists and marketing experts we have devised for the site of the disused home a truly unique leisure facility simulation. Open only to those under retirement age, but staffed entirely by ex-inmates of the home re-housed in premises to be built with grants from local government-backed enterprise initiative schemes – and perhaps even a few quid from yourselves if you can manage it – we are confident that this proposed theme park is far better suited to the current moral atmosphere than any boring scheme to offer decent care to the old and infirm.

TWERLY PARK

- **A day out for all the family!**
- **Educational, exciting, improving.**
- **Experience first-hand what it's really like to be elderly!**

As soon as you drive into the car park (just two minutes from the M1) you'll know you've entered the enchanting world of the elderly when you park your car and then queue for half an hour in the pouring rain for a private bus to the main site. There our highly trained guides are always on hand to patronize you. Some whisper, some bellow in your ear. All of them treat you like a mental defective as they lead you by the arm to places you don't want to go.

So much to see and do! One mock pension book of tickets gives you access to:

The Flatlet of Horrors

The floor shakes, the spectacles you're sure you put down somewhere a moment ago disappear and turn up again in unlikely places, the view out of the window is fuzzy and the small print of the *Radio Times* even smaller than usual.

The walls drip with condensation, the one-bar electric fire explodes when you switch it on. Now, put 10p in the slot and feel the temperature dropping. See for yourself how much knitting you can do before your bones freeze up!

Dead-end Street

Try walking slowly along a street made of foam rubber while cars and pedestrians whiz past at high speed. See if you can make it in one piece across the Zebra of Death! Made it? Watch out! The merry mugger's about . . .

Tape and Slide Show

Sentimentalized, rose-tinted images of bygone years mixed with state-of-the-art subliminal advertising techniques will implant radical precepts in the minds of even the most complacent of affluent nuclear family units.

Hands-On

School parties can make learning fun by trying out zimmerframes, surgical socks and heart pacemakers for themselves. Press a switch and feel an electric shock equivalent in pain level to that endured by a sufferer from chronic arthritis, put on earplugs and thick glasses and see if you can understand what the man in the post office is getting so agitated about when you try to pay your phone bill from your piggy bank of pennies . . .

Restaurant

Authentic Meals-On-Wheels-style food served by our buxom, genuine ex-social-service-employed dinner ladies. All vegetables guaranteed hardboiled!

Wheelchair Access

Kids especially will love the thrills and spills of the wheelchair ride. Feel your stomach drop as your chair is jolted up and down pavements, hurtles through puddles and collapses on you before sailing aloft to offer a dramatic aerial view of the entire park. Hold on tight, though!

Historical Re-enactments

Our troupe of professional actors, waiting to be offered good parts in panto, take you back in time to 'the olden days'.

Watch children being thrashed for no good reason declare: 'It never did us any harm.' Audience participation is welcome. Anyone who agrees with the kids can enjoy a good hiding themselves!

The World War 2 Experience: Re-live the street parties, the eccentric characters, the over-sexed Yanks, the camaraderie and community spirit, the huge sense of relief when the doodle-bug misses you and drops on the street next but one.

Be transported back to the days before TV when people made their own entertainment for the long winter evenings: sit in the dark twiddling your thumbs.

Plus such modern-day dramas as the tense opening moments of an Age Concern jumble sale!

And, for the ultimate experience, try:

It's Your Funeral

For a small additional fee, witness a personalized cremation, adapted just for you. Hear what your nearest and dearest will say about *you* after you're gone. Find out what rude witticism your family choose to have inscribed on the polystyrene novelty headstone which makes a lasting memento of your visit to treasure and keep.

Gift Shop

You can buy such attractive and tasteful souvenirs as:

- 'We Love Old Age' car stickers
- Miniature zimmerframe earrings
- False teeth necklaces
- Stick-on varicose veins
- Clothing for the kids which says: 'My family went to Twerly Park and all they bought me was this lousy thermal vest'.

Plus the ideal present to take home to the old folk: *Bluff Your Way in Nostalgia*.
Forgotten how much hotter the summers were then? How much friendlier folks were? What exactly it was you could buy for a tanner from the quaint corner shop and still have change? This slim volume fills you in on everything you need to think you know to impress your grandchildren with the way things were.

And, remember, all the gifts are guaranteed so costly that you too can reminisce about the day out at Twerly Park that left you poor – but happy!

On the Cruel Affliction of Juvenility

It's always terribly distressing when you see the tell-tale signs of this insidious condition developing in close associates, but I suppose it's unavoidable amongst people of my age group.

It can take some time to recognize the cause of those first minor symptoms – a tendency to forgetfulness, absent-mindedness, singing out of key at inopportune moments. Then suddenly the brain seizes up completely and it's all too clear. Juvenility has struck again.

I hate to say it, but I can see it happening now to Vera Totley. Just a few brief months ago she was just like any other perfectly normal paper-selling, public-speaking, rabble-rousing, far-left extremist. Then suddenly she began to dye her hair bright yellow and came bounding into HQ one tragic morning clad in track-suit and trainers.

Whilst on a routine check of the membership's coat pockets, I discovered her membership card to Agewell Anonymous. Things were looking grim.

It went from bad to worse. She sailed off on the Dreaded Cruise, came back brainwashed completely, beaming from ear to ear and showing us all snapshots of her in Benidorm, prancing about drunkenly with elderly Lotharios wearing cardboard sombreros. SAGA Louts, the lot of 'em.

We can't go on humouring her, not now she's trying to inflict her madness on the group with her blue-rinsed views on conservation and fitness funtime sessions. Wooing the woopy vote, she calls it. I'd rather woo leprosy.

I have not lived this long to spend my retirement pretending I was twelve again, prancing about in a leotard, twinkling my rheumy blue eyes and discussing private pension plans and the rejuvenative properties of Royal Jelly. I will not compete in some degrading game of Happy Grannies, each one outdoing the other in 'aren't-I-a-marvel-at-my-age-ism'. I know where it's leading: next minute it'll be last one to the health club gets euthanased.

'Ladies!' says Vera [I ask you!], 'you're as young as you feel!'

You're bloody well not, you know. Like blacks aren't as white as they feel, nor claimants as rich as they feel nor women as male. Being old is tough. Your bones ache, your faculties pack in, close friends die off at a faster rate than they once got divorced, the young abuse and patronize you – if they notice you at all.

Was it Shakespeare who once wrote 'Life is a fucker'? Perhaps not, but it's true all the same.

Certainly, if we stick together, show solidarity with our fellows, if we keep in sound heart and sound politics, we can better our lot. We deserve a decent pension, decent health care and the right to be left in peace to be and do what the bloody hell we want to. And we'll shout like red murder till we get what's our due.

No, I pity poor Vera, struck down in the prime of her life with this horrid affliction. She's living in a dream. But if that woman thinks she's got a cat in hell's chance of being elected Gen. Sec. at the next AGM she's got another think coming!

That woman takes power over my well body!

Our Day Out
by Doris Bendibus

This year's SPLAF annual beano to Scarborough was a great success I can gladly report! A good time was had by all (well, almost!).

To begin at the beginning: Up bright and early. Weather a bit foggy, but we live in hope! Make my sandwiches and prepare the Thermos. Mustn't forget to take an umbrella and extra cardie, tho'! Remember to make some extra sandwiches for Betty. Just one of my little duties as secretary of the SPLAF Ents Committee.

Sadly, Arnold's a bit poorly at present so I almost didn't come, but he urged me to go and enjoy myself, the dear. Left him some soup on the cooker, put an extra plate of Kattomeat out for Leonid and headed off to the bus stop.

Outside the coach station, meet up with the rest of our 'merry band'. Much chatter about Vera's decision to put herself forward as a candidate for Gen. Sec. I comment to B. how delighted she must be that others in the group now feel confident enough to stand for positions previously won by B. uncontested.

Very soon the coach sets off and we're on our way at last! What a very pleasant view I have from my cosy seat by the window. I have seldom seen the new Budgen's Megastore looking so beautiful as it does today, clad as it is in its fetherlite raiment of drizzle.

B. sat beside me. Appears to be suffering from travel sickness tho'. I offer her my seat, of course, but she still seems ill at ease somehow. Every time I ask how she is, she tells me to 'go boil my head' and 'put a sock in it' and other quaint local expressions. 'You are a one, Betty!' I quip, to which B. replies with her

customary wit, 'B****r off!', which somewhat amuses me.

I try to cheer her up by telling anecdotes concerning my youngest's two lively kiddies. I can tell that B. is secretly enjoying my tales of the antics of these delightful young scamps.

Eric Moorfoot reads in the papers that the CBI conference is in session this week at the Royale in Scarborough. Ever the activist, Eric suggests that we picket it. But B. not keen. 'Can't we forget about politics for just one day of the year?' she pleads.

Much excitement about where our Magical Mystery Tour will take us for light refreshment. Great relief when our driver pulls up, as always, at our favourite, the Happy Chefette. Highly recommended. Staff, food and toilets as clean, warm and fresh as you like!

Betty and I listen fascinated as Vera outlines her plans to revamp the account system, should she be elected. Never realized V's husband had worked for many years in the Fraud Squad. I don't think Betty had either, somehow.

Quite a shock for Vera to find herself trapped in the lavatory (which, by the way, a kind note therein assures us are cleaned on the hour every hour). V. only just managed to flag down the coach in time. I was trying to tell the driver that one of our number was absent when Betty leapt aboard, crying out to the driver, 'Agitate the gravel, sunbeam!' Poor dear. I do so fret about these turns of hers.

A good singsong is had by all. But I wish B. would realize we don't all know the words to some of these old songs. How many readers can recall the chorus of 'We Don't Need That Fascist Groove Thang', I wonder?

On arrival we set off in groups, some to the front, some to the amusement arcades and shops. Health-conscious as always, Vera changes into her track-suit and sets off for a sprint along south pier. An inspiration to all!

I hire a deckchair and sit on the beach, in a happy reverie of memories of bygone days. How well I remember the chara rides we had as kiddies – when we were given two paper-bags to take on the trip, one filled with sandwiches and one to be sick in. After strolling down the prom to watch the pierrots and Punch and Judy, spending our few precious pennies on such favourites as sherbert doings and creamy abdabs, we'd tuck our frocks into our knickers and paddle the day long, happy as sandboys! What is a sandboy, I wonder? Oh, well . . . Pleasant days!

Wake to find B. asleep beside me, snoring heavily and clutching a bottle of some kind of beverage. She's wearing a lovely novelty tee-shirt purchased, I assume, from a souvenir shop. A very attractive shade of green. On the front in black letters: WOOPIES SUCK. The green goes very well with her pretty new cap, a jolly symbol of peace in these strife-torn times: red with pink peak and two felt fingers sticking out of the top of it.

Vera returns to share her salad sandwiches and registers her wish for a dip. Brrrr! Rather her than me! Betty dissuades her; she has all the gen about levels of radioactivity and our close proximity to the sewage farm, but kindly offers to take Vera to a new private swimming-pool she's heard all about.

In the afternoon I while away a blissful hour in Woolies, buying gifts for the grandchildren and some bright new pyjamas for Arnold to help raise his spirits. Bump into Betty filling her bag with electrical appliances. Point out the sign saying all goods to be placed in the wire baskets provided and she thanks me so kindly.

Just time for a turn round the gardens and poignant thoughts of that summer with Arnold who always did so like to sit here and look at the birds. Then it's back to the coach.

Get home, weary but happy, just in time for a good chinwag with Arnold before 'News at Ten'. Item about an elderly streaker disrupting CBI Conference. Apparently a security man heard suspicious knockings from a broom cupboard. He unlocked it only to find an elderly lady struggling out of her girdle, which she handed him shouting, 'Last one in's a biddy!' and dived out, straight on to the main platform. Imagine my surprise to recognize none other than Vera Totley being carried away by six handsome policemen!

Phone Betty who says she didn't know Vera had it in her. A shame to lose such a much-loved and dedicated member. It seems next year's Magical Mystery Tour may have to be to Holloway. Be sure to book early, won't you?

Minutes of the SPLAF AGM

Present: E. Moorfoot (Chair), B. Spital (Gen. Sec.), D. Bendibus (Sec. – and I took the minutes, of course), A. Bendibus (Treasurer), V. Totley (fortunately back with us after her unfortunate incident. Her brother's a lawyer, I hear), S. Netheredge, A. Glossop, L. Hackenthorpe, R. Gleadless, M. Peacegardens.

Apologies: W. Bakewell (Thank goodness! Actually he didn't sound terribly apologetic, but he did say he wasn't coming. Something to do with the gasman and angels.)

AGENDA: I could have sworn I had it scribbled on a bus ticket in my bag first thing this morning. I do hope I didn't put it in with my letter to our Frank in Sydney.

1 The minutes of the last meeting were read and passed as an accurate-ish record, though I was asked if I could refrain from doodling in the margins. Point taken, Comrades!

2 Report by Stan Netheredge on the Policy Review Sub-Committee. See paper attached. Very interesting, I'm sure, though I do wish Stan would heed my requests to him to speak up.

Vera said – very audibly – that she thought it was super, full of terribly good ideas about popular appeal, but did it need to have all that turgid rhetorical nonsense in it? We were all entitled to our own views but the main thing was unity and she couldn't see why politics always had to get caught up in it. A lively debate ensued. (You can say that again!)

3 Elections

SECRETARY: D. Bendibus re-elected unopposed (except by me!).

TREASURER: Arnold declared with regret that he no longer felt able to continue in this post. Vote of thanks for all his splendid work over the years, which was nice.

But no one else seemed prepared to stand as his replacement as it does involve an awful lot of work, as I well know. In her absence A. Overleaf was co-opted on to the Committee as an Honorary Twerly, which Betty assured us she'd be delighted by at her age.

A. Overleaf elected Treasurer unopposed.

Proposal by B. Spital that, in view of her long-standing record as an energetic and inspired communicator, Vera Totley should be put forward for a new post of voluntary outreach worker in Barnsley.

Vera stated that, flattered as she was, she'd rather had her eye on another job, but Betty most insistent that this one would most benefit from Vera's enormous skills and capabilities.

Passed unanimously.

Betty to supply map of how precisely V. to reach her outpost.

GENERAL SECRETARY: Vera proposed that in view of B. Spital's even longer-standing record as a great leader, perhaps the time had come to create the post of Honorary President and leave the arduous task of day-to-day running of the organization to someone else. Betty supported the creation of the new post.

B. Spital elected Honorary President unopposed.

However, B. then assured us she felt fit as a fiddle and was quite positive she could handle both jobs at once, thank you.

V. proposed that well, at least, surely it would be better to turn the job of Gen. Sec. into a jobshare, giving our beloved leader some time for other leisure pursuits. B. showed her preparedness to struggle on alone but V. insistent and kindly volunteered herself as co-leader, as the outreach post would only be part-time.

But B. suddenly remembered a point in the constitution which states that the role of Gen. Sec. can only be occupied by one person at a time. V. said she thought this most old-fashioned. B. agreed wholeheartedly but apparently it would be illegal to proceed without an extraordinary general meeting which could take some time to arrange. V. keen to arrange a date, B. unfortunately couldn't find her diary.

Decision to defer decision till next meeting.

B. then pointed out that if V. was in need of further duties to occupy her, there was no reason why the outreach job shouldn't be made full-time.

4 E. Moorfoot gave the meeting a detailed account of his weekend in Hastings. Thanked by the Chair for his fascinating intervention.

5 Request for donation from Anglo-Soviet Society

V. spoke most movingly about how vital it was to support Glasnost and the new spirit of openness in Russia which had swept away corruption from high government circles.

B. agreed entirely and told us how much she identified with Mister Gorbachev, besieged on one side by party hacks and on the other by the forces of capitalism. I'm not quite sure what she meant about the far-reaching programme of reforms she'd introduced recently at SPLAF, but she did put a sign on the photocopier afterwards saying from now on members didn't need to get permission in writing from her each time they needed to use it.

6 Report from Finance Sub.

Vera about to begin her report when Betty unfortunately had one of her rare seizures and collapsed. Then Arnold did too and I thought he was joking at first but he wasn't.

7 Any Other Business

I stayed with him in the hospital till late; he was sleeping most of the time which was probably the drugs. Then this very nice nurse told me perhaps I ought to go home and have some rest as she was sure he was settled for the night now. I got ever so upset having to leave him like that, but he woke up for a moment and smiled and whispered he loved me and said I should go. So I kissed him on the cheek and said I'd be back first thing in the morning and bring in some bananas and went.

On the New Magic Realism

*Paper by the Manifesto Working Party of the
SPLAF Policy Review*

> *Nah then – aye allus reckon'd: tha reet eesy werds
> moost be enuff. Wenn aye sez ow things is goin off
> Awl ys harts'd bi tawnta shreds,
> Thatyer'll git shatton ifya dohnt stund oop fer thissen –
> 'Sreet chuffin obviuhs intit?*
>
> BERTOLT BRECHT (trans. A BENDIBUS)

The harsh blue wind of Thatcherism has been blowing through this land so long now that it's increasingly difficult for those on the left to do anything more active than jump up and down to avoid hypothermia. What's more, the political climate has had a traumatic effect upon the collective consciousness of the population as a whole.

What we are witnessing is no less than the Senility of Capitalism, that phase of societal development so astutely predicted in early Marxist-Spitalist analyses.

The symptoms of this phase are these: gradual loss of memory, increasing rigidity of attitudes, confusion, paranoia, mental derangement, meanness, bursts of frenetic activity and self-obsession.

In a society where our history has been minced and reconstituted into a tasteless quiksnak for tourist consumption, in which bigotry is applauded and fear of redundancy haunts all those in the workforce, in which people are driven to slave harder and harder in pursuit of illusory dreams of success as the self-employed Kissagrams of post-industrial enterprise culture,

171

where state benefits to the poor have been seriously eroded and tax cuts dished out to the too-bloody-rich-for-their-own-good-already, the insidious development of this debilitating condition has become all too clear.

Strident demands by the left for 'direct action', 'struggle' and yet more fightbacks against yet more cutbacks fall on ears grown hard of hearing. The voters of this country are tired, jumpy, hypertense, confused. They need reassurance, they want to be led by the hand to a metaphorical comfortable chair and told kindly but firmly to take things easy and have a break from it all.

'Put Your Feet up – Vote for Us' is a far more attractive slogan than 'Onward to Victory'.

Market research reveals a deep-seated desire for retirement amongst people of all ages and points to the huge electoral advantages of couching SPLAF policies in language which speaks directly to the pensioner within us all.

Thus:

Out go outmoded demands for the eradication of unemployment and an increase in part-time work, conservation, education and arts for all, internationalist anti-racist immigration policy and unilateral nuclear disarmament.

In comes a manifesto suggesting lowering the retirement age to thirty-five, leaving time for hobbies, a spot of gardening, evening classes, reading, sketching and Bingo, friendly neighbours and no loud noises.

Out go calls for demonstrations urging General Strikes and Armed Insurrections. No more marching through the rain shouting 'Maggie Maggie Maggie Out Out Out' to a line of bored policemen.

In with proposals for mass walking tours of our picturesque inner cities.

We've still failed to crack an entirely convincing method of making the overthrow of the existing means of production sound like a coach trip to Skegness, but do have high hopes for a winning comparison between violent revolution and old people's noted fondness for all-in wrestling.

Arise ye Twerlies from your snoozes!
No more they'll call ye 'sweet old dear'
Betty's thundrous trump hath sounded,
Second Childhood draweth near.

It's the current government's policies which lead towards heart failure and an early grave. Only SPLAF can bring about true regeneration – heralding the coming of a new era.

SECOND CHILDHOOD is a return to playfulness, a shedding of the onerous responsibilities of middle age, the awakening of a shared sense of solidarity through the common bond of elder-liness, a turning away from wasteful materialism towards enjoy-ment of life's simple pleasures.

SECOND CHILDHOOD is the dawning of a social conscious-ness which spurns macho notions of decisiveness and force to celebrate such much-maligned qualities as:

ditheriness: born of a recognition of the surreal complexities of the modern world
stroppiness: vital in defending our rights against attack
eccentricity: an affirmation of the uniqueness of the individual, a quality which allows us to look at problems with a new creativity

Finally, if the present Prime Minister appeals to the Nation's desire to be nannied, it is our belief that Spital could have massive appeal to the electorate as a favourite baby-sitter or eccentric Great Aunt, the sort who offers children sips of her sherry, tells them rude stories about their parents and lets them stay up.

Admittedly our General Secretary's image will have to be slightly remodelled to enhance her more humane aspects, but this is nothing that elocution lessons, a change of wardrobe, intensive psychotherapy and plastic surgery can't achieve.

SO RAISE THE TWERLY STANDARD HIGH –
WE'VE LOTS TO DO BEFORE WE DIE!

DON'T VEGETATE – AGITATE!

CHEER UP, COMRADES – THE FUTURE LOOKS GREY!

173

From a phototherapy

session on shopping

On Youthanasia

I know how young people complain about the old making their lives a misery, so we at SPLAF feel strongly that we should put them out of their suffering. FREE YOUTHANASIA ON DEMAND – A TWERLY'S RIGHT TO CHOOSE, that's our motto. If the young can't be bothered to look after their elders, then kill 'em I say!

Well, how do you think we pensioners feel seeing the flesh of our flesh getting into misguided ways: sons getting jobs as bankers, girls marrying?

Don't get me wrong – it'd be voluntary. Old people could decide for themselves which of their offspring to have put down. And we'd be doing you a favour, thinning the ranks so there's more room in old people's homes when you get old. You as survive.

So if you want to take a hand in building a better world of love, equality and understanding, vote SPLAF.

If you don't, then you can drop dead, age-traitor.

On the Art of Dying

Let's be honest, dying is no laughing matter.

One of my colleagues at SPLAF passed on the other week. A sweet old man, one of the kindest, most good-tempered, fair-minded, inoffensive people you could possibly meet. Not my type you might think, but I admit, I were upset. Arnold Bendibus and I went back a long way.

Went to his do at the Crem. When you get to my age you find yourself going to a lot of funerals. You get into a sort of routine. I always take a Thermos in case it gets chilly – and my knitting – and my Sony Walkman.

Shoving all the dead together in graveyards seems mistaken to me. Like sticking dangerous criminals in prison together, or sending the depressed off to a place full of the even more bloody miserable. Community Aftercare I'd like to introduce, so you'd scatter 'em about more, integrate the dead into the rest of society. Bung your deceased granny in a graveyard and you need never think of her again – but if each time you backed the hatchback out of the drive you had to navigate round the headstone she really would be *ever in your thoughts*.

I went with Doris to the undertakers. I'm afraid I got the giggles. Well, they're so – very – very – slow – about – ev – er – y – thing. Bet they speed up at the end of the day when they're counting the takings.

And what if you come to work one day feeling absolutely fantastic? Probably grounds for instant dismissal.

He says to us, 'May I suggest this very reasonable mid-price mahogany casket with tooled velvet interior? Or, of course, there's the cheap cloth-covered one . . .'

I says to him, 'We're only having Arnold cremated. Can't you save his widow here a bob or two and just pop him in a bin liner?'

'Madam, you don't think that might appear somewhat disrespectful?' he says to me, bold as you like.

I says, 'Don't come tooled velvet interiors with me, bumface. We're talking about marking the end of a man's life, not about bloody Filofax accessories.'

Well, the whole thing makes me so angry!

As soon as I was back from the funeral, I got straight on the phone. Complained to the hospital about cutbacks in staff, to the DHSS about stopping the death allowance, to the Council about the state of the house he were living in, to the local paper for editing his obituary (Doris wanted to say: 'Much missed — especially in bed'). I complained to the crematorium about the dogshit in the Garden of Remembrance; I even left a message on Maggie Thatcher's Ansaphone telling her she could drop dead and all.

Then I hung up. Just sat there. Couldn't think of anyone else left to blame.

Agenda Again

Just me again – Agenda – butting in to sayy how marvellous it's been tyyping Betyyy's book for her. I mean, the things one learns; it's an education honestlyy y and anyy w a y y y y y y y y y y y y y y y y y y y y y y y y y y y y y y y y y y y – Whoops, sorr about that. Sproggo was sick over the keyy y y y y y yboard earlier and one of the letters has got rather glunked up. I'll just pop and get a J-Cloth.

Y Y Y Y Y Y Yes. That's better. Anyway, as you may gather, the Babe has arrived. Still a bit stumped about names. Nicko likes Henry, Betty suggests Ilyich and mum's gunning for Geoffrey.

And, yes, it's a boy. Sorry. And he's absolutely gorgeous and perfect and wonderful and I know I get terribly boring about him and mustn't go on, not even about this *sweet* little tuft of ginger hair he's got which makes him look ever so much like Neil Kinnock – crossed with ET.

Betty's been popping round a lot since the birth. I was so sorry to hear about Mr Bendibus. Not that I knew him very well personally but Doris is a sweetie and I know Betty's very upset about it all, and I'm sure that's why she's been complaining quite so much about Sproggy crying in the night.

I do think it's marvellous how *up front* Betty is about sex and things. Quite amazing for someone that age because I suppose in a way I thought it was only people like us who were like that. I mean were like that *once*, or at least tried to be, until it all went out of fashion with AIDS and whathaveyou.

Funny how that happens. One minute something's the Great Burning Issue of Our Times and the next minute just isn't any more and you're not quite sure why. Like flared trousers.

Though Nicko and I still have an utterly open relationship; it's absolutely taken as read that if either of us ever fancied anybody else, ever however slightly, then it was our absolute right to go straight ahead and get on with it. Get stuck in, sort of thing. It's just that neither of us has done, as yet – fancied it, that is.

I tell a lie because Nicko did once have a bit of a snog with this Kathy girl (sorry, woman) at an office party and apparently it was mutual. I mean not very serious on his part but a bit – Well, you just can't quantify things like that as he said at the time, but the whole thing was really just a sort of wild spontaneous urge to do something totally irresponsible and crazy and carefree for a change. And I'm all for that, of course. I mean, good grief, life's too short, etcetera.

So we invited her round and laid our cards on the table. I asked her a few questions about her attitude to primary relationships and commitment over a vegetable curry and by the end I said to her, 'I do think you're super, just his type, and I'm sure you'll do fine and he's terribly good in bed, on the whole, so I'm sure you'll have fun and we can work out a rota so that I can ask mum up to stay to be sure I have company.' And afterwards Nicko and I felt marvellous. Terribly freed.

But Kathy never phoned Nick again.

And then there was Kenny from work, of course. But that was quite quite different. Nicko got so terribly upset that I couldn't possibly have gone through with it, though I was rather nuts on Ken at the time. Nicko wasn't bothered at all by the idea of his (sorry!) wife having it off with another man, of course, but for far more important, psychological reasons. Which escape me for the present. Anyway. The stitches and the nightfeed knock bonking of all forms on the head at the present.

What set me thinking about that? Babies. Time. Age. What have you. Worrying about what sort of a society I went through such agonies to push poor Sprog out into.

I'm sorry but I've agonized over this one for ages and I really don't think it's all my fault that there's been absolutely no decent opposition whatsoever to that rotten Thatcher woman for all these years. God, I hate her I hate her I hate her, which just goes to show how little I like her – if the truth be told. But I do feel so guilty.

I mean, oh God, this is embarrassing but, yes, I did once have a sexy dream about David Owen in the early days of the SDP when it was the trendy media darling, when I was going through this terrible oh-take-me-you-smarmy-great-beast-of-a-man sort of phase after the Kenneth thing. But that was years ago. Now I could kick myself for being so wooed.

I know Betty wouldn't be. She'd hang on to her ideological loons come hell and high water and good on her.

Let's hope Henry Ilyich Geoffrey Sprog Overleaf turns out like that. (Talk of the devil. He's just started howling!) I took him down to see Mr Bendibus when I discovered he was in the same wing of the hospital and it was amazing to see Sprog's teeny weeny little fingers wrapped round Arnold's wizened digit.

Oh, dear. I get terribly emotional at the moment and keep getting this lump in my throat and feeling like I'm about to voice something really profound and moving and new – and I open my mouth and out pours green poo and nappyrash and breast versus bottle. Must be all these hormones still whooshing around. So I'm sorry if I'm rambling rather. I must be getting old.

Gosh! Won't Betty be pleased!

Radical Alternatives to the Funeral

Death holds no sting for me. I've led a long and active life after all, and, anyway, when I cross over to the other side I know there'll be so much to do. The dead must be the largest remaining group in society still to lack proper trade union representation. The TUC may be on its last legs, but the Union of All Souls and Allied Wraiths has a long and bright future before it, you mark my words.

And this brutal apartheid system which divides saints and sinners is vile and outmoded. It's just got to go.

Meanwhile, the item at the top of my agenda is how precisely to finish things here. You won't catch me shuffling, Comrades, when the time comes to evacuate this mortal coil!

Political martyrdom has always had a great appeal for me. I felt ever such an empathy with Bobby Sands when we met him on our works outing to Long Kesh.

'Bob,' I said to him, 'I only wish I were in your shoes.'

'Betty,' he said to me, 'so do I.'

Being shot through the heart by a jealous wife finding me in bed with her gorgeous young husband would be nice for the ego, but since the AIDS scare we Twerlies have vowed only to bonk with our own.

Or there's the gradualist approach: a good, slow wasting disease with hordes of my fans and supporters amassed outside the hospital for daily briefings on my condition, plenty of time for the media people to prepare their obituaries and retrospective seasons, etcetera, while a handful of my closest disciples sit in silent, tearful vigil round my bedside, awaiting my Final Great Thought.

But what if I fluffed it? I'm not having them announce on 'Newsnight' that Betty Spital departed this life with the words 'Stick them in a vase, will you, Doris?' on her lips!

And then there's the send-off. I know some of the more libertarian sections of the pensioners movement favour replacing conventional funerals altogether with Death Affirmation Workshops, where everyone has to list ten reasons why it must be great for the deceased being dead and then ten more reasons why, to be honest, it's a bit of a relief for those present too.

The Maoist contingent used to go in for headstones which said things like: IN LOVING MEMORY OF OUR BELOVED COMPANION, MUCH MISSED DESPITE THOSE DECADENT TENDENCIES WHICH SHE NEVER QUITE MANAGED TO SUPPRESS THROUGH STRENUOUS SELF-CRITICISM.

Leaving bits of your body to help further the course of medical knowledge sounded good to me, till I came across this medical student on a rag week pyjama jump, and that put me right off. In Tibet apparently they leave the body out on a rock for the vultures to nibble which sounds very ecologically sound. Though granted round our way I might become something of a public health risk before the pigeons got round to picking me dry.

In our classes on Dying As a Campaigning Tool we suggest ensuring that relations put your corpse to some active use, say by dumping it mysteriously close to a nuclear power station or planting it in a queue for housing benefit and then phoning the media.

An old flame of mine was cremated and then scattered on the beach at Scarborough, which seemed fitting. Only trouble was the wind. I chucked a handful of my beloved towards the sea but it blew back and the whole lot flew straight up my skirt. Which was just typical of him as it happens.

But personally I'd like a Lenin: full embalming and a nice location for my lying-in-state – say just next to the breakfast cereals in our local Safeway's – so as people would have to file past respectfully on their way to the checkout.